D1074967

Books by Ephraim Kishon

Wise Guy, Solomon

Ephraim Kishon

Wise Guy, Solomon

TRANSLATED FROM THE HEBREW BY YOHANAN GOLDMAN

Atheneum NEW YORK *1973*

The Supreme Royal Court

Jerusalem

Your Honors,

In my capacity as attorney representing the mother who was the winning party in the famous Solomon's Judgment, I herewith take the liberty of appealing His Majesty's verdict. As recorded in the court minutes, my client underwent cross-examination in the King's Court seventeen years ago, and, following the King's order to split the baby whose parentage was in doubt and give each woman an equal half, my client emitted a shout to the legally incontestable effect that she was RENOUNCING any claim to the child. All the same, for reasons best known to himself, His Majesty ruled as he did and awarded custody of the baby to my client.

In the meantime, the baby in question has grown up and is now covered with long, matted hair and smokes large amounts of grass. Furthermore, he dresses like a scarecrow with strong leftist leanings and idles away his time in dubious discotheques, all this at the expense of my indigent client because of the unfortunate verdict in which she was appointed "natural mother," without any factual or laboratory proof.

Therefore, I herewith appeal His Majesty's verdict. My client declares that the shout attributed to her constituted a complete and final disclaimer of kinship toward the baby in question. My client furthermore requests an early retrial, in order to transfer motherhood of the brat to the other woman, failing which my client will adopt the only logical course of action and kick the lazy bum out of her apartment.

Contents

Wise Guy, Solomon

❦ Humor as such is considered a sort of by-product of the literary industry, but in journalism it is relegated to the task of boiler plate for filling typographical gaps on badly laid-out pages. "Quick, get me two columns of humor in eleven-point Cicero," the editor shouts at his slaves over the clanking of the linotype machines, and at once the gooey stuff is poured to the bottom of the page, freely filling the empty space. This is called "free press."

A Little Publicity

The chief editor of the popular magazine *Epess* roared a summons to Ziegler, the assistant editor for literature and acting sports writer, and dragged him over the coals.

"The paper is boring as hell," the chief editor said. "We've got to liven it up at all costs. Have you got a twenty-line joke or something?"

"Yes," Ziegler replied, bursting with suppressed laughter. "I heard a good one on the way to the office. Zungspitz the bookkeeper comes up to his boss. 'Sir, I'd like to go to my mother-in-law's funeral.' The boss answers, 'You know what, Zungspitz? So would I!' That is, he too, the boss, would like to go to his mother-in-law's funeral. . . . Good, isn't it . . . I haven't stopped laughing since this morning."

"An idiotic and disgusting joke, and besides, we've already printed it at least twice," the chief editor hissed glacially. "There is only one way of saving such a miserable joke: It must be credited to some artist, actor, writer or other parasite. As a matter of fact, I read only today that Tola'at Sha'ani's play has bombed-out dismally."

"But wouldn't he be furious?"

"Furious? Because of a little publicity? Is that all you know about those guys?"

Next day the "What's New, Boys" column featured the following intimate story headed "Bulls-eye!":

Itzhak Tola'at Sha'ani, the promising author, the other day gave conclusive proof that his well-known sense of humor has not been impaired by the panning his play received. As is his custom, the writer was roaming the Knesset lobbies at dusk when suddenly his driver walked up to him.

"Mr. Tola'at Sha'ani, I'd like to go to my mother-in-law's funeral."

The writer's spontaneous answer did not fail to materialize: "You know what, Zungspitz, so would I!"

The dozen or so people within earshot, including some of the heads of the Coalition, rewarded the quip with loud and prolonged laughter.

Itzhak Tola'at Sha'ani does not as a rule read the popular magazine *Epess*, therefore he did not understand for two days why all his acquaintances were avoiding him in the street. Then he received a registered letter from his mother-in-law spiced with Russian idioms. "If you are so completely lacking in respect," his wife's mother wrote, "at least don't kill me with such a coarse and hoary joke. You are a fool."

The greatly upset writer made desperate efforts to correct the terrible impression his stupid joke had left. He buttonholed everybody in his favorite café and went on for hours to the effect that he had never visited the

Knesset, had no car and certainly no driver, and for goodness' sake who was Zungspitz? But no one paid any attention to his excuses, because everybody knows that there is no smoke without fire, and it was out of the question that a magazine would simply invent such things. What particularly irked people was the way the writer had tried to butter up the Coalition heads. However, though they despised Tola'at Sha'ani, the tens of thousands of readers were angry at the editor of the magazine, who in a moment of weakness, or because of a flaw in his character, had not rejected the request of this young publicity hound, this maniac, and had played along with him.

Tola'at Sha'ani did what every honest person would have done in similar circumstances: He retained a lawyer. He handed over the offending issue of *Epess* to Dr. Shai-Shonberger and said to him; "Read!"

After reading the joke the lawyer burst out laughing. "Excellent. I didn't realize you had such an excellent sense of humor."

"Sir," said Tola'at Sha'ani—who, by the way, is a serious and very reserved person—"I respect my mother-in-law and don't ever poke fun at her."

The lawyer wiped the smile off his face. "I see. Then why do you tell such stupid jokes?"

The writer described in detail the surprise element which characterized the whole miserable affair. In Dr. S.-S.'s view a libel suit against the magazine was certainly justified, but such suits as a rule take three to four years before they are settled and in the end you always lose, because in the meantime the judges have forgotten what it was all about. The writer and his lawyer decided, therefore, to send a warning letter to the editor of *Epess* and demand a complete retraction:

. . . I was shocked to read in your magazine a stale joke attributed to me without my permission. Therefore you are herewith requested to provide suitable moral amends to myself and my mother-in-law, who enjoys perfect health and maintains harmonious family relations with me. I herewith further request that you publish an apology within a week from the receipt of this letter, failing which I shall consider myself free to . . .

"You've put us in a nice spot, Ziegler, I must say," the editor-in-chief upbraided his assistant. "Tola'at Sha'ani is asking for an apology from me."

"*Oy*," said Ziegler. "I told you he'd be furious."

"Furious?" the editor scoffed, supported by twenty-three years of rich journalistic experience. "He's beside himself with joy! Don't you realize that all he asks from us is to get some more free publicity? You make a nice gesture, you let them run once, so right away they come back at you clamoring for more. Never mind what you write about them, how you write, as long as you simply mention their names."

"The hypocrites," Ziegler agreed.

"Never mind," said the editor. "I'll write some sort of apology in his name, a letter maybe. Though I must say he could at least have written it himself. Ziegler, fetch me the first volume of *A Treasury of Jokes*."

Tola'at Sha'ani read the reply in a dark corner of the café, and the pages of the magazine shook in his hands like leaves in a strong wind. Under the heading "Letter of Apology," he read:

As a faithful reader of your excellent paper I must confess that I greatly enjoyed your excellent joke about my mother-in-law's funeral. Congratulations. In all fairness, however, I must apologize. Unfortunately, I did not personally invent this remarkable joke. My mother-in-law, thank God, is as healthy as a horse. What's more, she always cooks my favorite dishes. In this connection, dear editor, I'd like to tell you what happened at our place a few days ago. As I was passing a pet shop my eyes fell on a big parrot, who, according to the shopkeeper, spoke seven languages. I bought the bird and had it sent home by the shop messenger. But what do you think happened next? I did not know that my wife had arranged to have a chicken sent home from the butcher's. In short, the parrot arrived and, through a regrettable error, ended his career in my mother-in-law's cooking pot. At lunchtime I discovered the poor fellow on my plate and shouted, "For goodness' sake, this parrot spoke seven languages."

"Oh yeah?" my mother-in-law replied. "Then why didn't he speak up?"

Yours admiringly,
Itzhak Tola'at Sha'ani

The café staff and patrons watched, fascinated and somewhat alarmed, as the promising writer threw the popular magazine to the floor and then stomped on it, his face contorted with rage, babbling incoherently. Those who had read the latest issues of *Epess* could not feel any sympathy toward the writer, because his latest primitive quip about the parrot and his mother-in-law was really in shockingly bad taste. Driver, Knesset, parrot, languages—what would he think of next? What infantile gibberish was this anyway? Tola'at Sha'ani stumbled home and found his apartment empty. His wife had gone home to her mother, leaving behind a one-word message: "Mad!" Later on the neighbors heard the writer chopping up the furniture with an ax, but they did not intervene because they knew from the newspaper accounts that he was completely demented.

After T.S. had demolished the apartment, he grabbed a dull kitchen knife, took a taxi to the *Epess* office and burst through the editor-in-chief's door.

"You bastard!" Tola'at Sha'ani croaked in a strange voice, brandishing the knife. "Is this your apology?"

The editor drew himself up to his full height. "My apology? You must be joking. I should apologize for giving you the free publicity you keep begging from me? Look, sir, instead of thanking me for turning your cinder-dry letter into something sparkling with humor, you have the nerve to ask for more? What's the matter with you? Put that knife away, Tola'at, or else so help me I'll kick your ass from here to the seashore!"

The writer dropped the knife. He had very little experience with such things.

"I," he whispered, "didn't write anything about parrots."

"Your letter was slightly edited," the editor admitted. "Any material we publish is adapted to the paper's general editorial policy. We are not your private mouthpiece, my friend, in which you can publish anything that comes to your mind. What would you like me to do?"

"I want a retraction," T.S. sobbed. "A small correction. This is no joking matter, sir. My mother-in-law hasn't spoken to me for two weeks."

The editor relented. "All right." He was really a softhearted person. "Though our circulation is based on the confidence our readers have in the reliability of our sources of information, we'll make an exception in your case. I'll publish a little erratum, naturally couched in excellent humor, elegant . . ."

"No! Not in excellent humor! Not elegantly!" the writer yelled. He dropped to his knees and clung to the editor's legs, but Ziegler quickly detached him and chased him away.

Left alone, the editor mused, "They'd kill you to get a little publicity."

Three days later, under the heading "Erratum," a pearl of a story appeared under the subheading "The Mother-in-Law Does Not Answer." The article also featured a blurred photograph of Tola'at Sha'ani dug out of the magazine morgue. It had been taken nine years before at a buffet held by the Polish Circus just as the writer was choking on a lettuce sandwich.

Tola'at Sha'ani, whose play has now been definitely removed from the repertory, is spending his considerable leisure on the Caesarea golf links. At a cordial meeting with our correspondent, the promising playwright expressed his "annoyance" because we had published in our magazine some extremely funny jokes about his mother-in-law, whom he fondly loves.

"This is no joking matter," T.S. complained. "My mother-in-law hasn't spoken to me for two weeks."

"Is she that furious?"

"Worse. She sprained her chin and can't move her tongue."

"And what does the doctor say?"

"The doctor?" Tola'at Sha'ani grinned whimsically. "He wanted to come at once. I said to him, 'What's the hurry? Come in a fortnight.'"

And with that the writer hit the ball, which whooshed through the air, whistling gaily.

The first stone smashed through the windowpane at about lunchtime. But Tola'at Sha'ani had succeeded in escaping from his home before the demonstration got under way in earnest. He walked the streets, hugging the walls in the darkness, on his way to an isolated border settlement in the south; but a few steps from the bus station his mother-in-law caught up with him and started to beat him over the head with her umbrella.

At the hospital the doctor avoided talking to him. Golf? Caesarea? Sprained chin? All the same, he received proper treatment in the alcoholics' ward. Bandaged up to his eyes and dejected, T.S. reclined on a couch, sending a fervent prayer heavenward.

"Good Lord," his cracked lips whispered, "how can I break the spell? How?"

In a blinding flash an angel descended from heaven, in his hands the sword of democracy and on his head a crown of press freedom. The angel stopped next to the writer's bed and said, "Submit a bill."

The Epess Editorial Office
Here

Sir, In the last three issues of your magazine you were kind enough to publish three of my short satirical stories:

1. Zungspitz and the Funeral
2. Why Did the Parrot Keep Quiet?
3. Right on the Chin

Please forward my writer's fee by return mail.

Ever since—at long last—there has been blessed quiet.

❦ *Besides the female sex, there exists another commodity that modern male can neither live with nor do without: the telephone. This is a sort of drug addiction; therefore we hate the sadistic instrument which makes our lives a misery with its sudden ringing. On the other hand we could not live even a day without it. Right? If ever a few hours go by without dialing, we are gripped by an acute Angst, our hand starts shaking slightly, the dialing finger gets an erection and is drawn irresistibly to any available dial. Following is a confession of a terminal telephone addict.*

Telephokinetics

It looks as if we have got over the Age of Telepathy. Svengali no longer glares at us from his posters, yet he has not given a definite answer to the question: Do such things exist or don't they? And now this writer is all on his own in the field of Mediterranean telepathy.

Our act has not yet been exploited by any impresario; it takes place in our house, in the narrow corridor leading from our desk to the bathroom. It has something to do with numbers. We go to the bathroom, lock the door, undress and turn on the shower. The moment we start soaping our back—listen to this—at that very instant the phone starts ringing. Always. We have become so accustomed to this telepathic act that at a certain point in the soaping we stop and wait passively for the ring. And it always comes. Naturally, we could simply disregard it. One can pretend one does not hear any ringing above the rush of the water, or else one can say to oneself, "I'm not at home." But that is unrealistic, because one is at home, is one not? The hot water stimulates the imagination. We imagine that behind every sudsy ring a very fat man with a cigar in his mouth is sitting at the other end of the line in New York, dying to turn us into a smash Broadway musical.

So we go to the phone. We can't help it. We wash off the soap in a frenzy, wrap a towel around our shoulders and run with odd little skips through rooms in which all the windows are wide open, until we get to the telephone. And then the ringing stops. Or else someone says at the other end, "Pardon me, is Uzzi there?" What Uzzi? we ask, and then someone quietly puts down the receiver, and all that's left is a puddle on the floor.

We return to the shower, drop the wet towel, sneeze and jump back under the pleasant stream. We soak our back properly and the phone rings. Now we have two alternatives: If we don't go, at the other end there is the fat man, the cigar and the musical. If we go it's Uzzi again.

Telephokinetics—the art of moving people by soaping.

The wife claims that I'm talking nonsense, that there is nothing occult in this. Nobody calls because I'm taking a shower; it's the other way around. I feel that someone is about to call me, so I start soaping myself. In any case, there is some sort of mutual influence. For instance, I'll never forget the night of October 13 when I sat for hours on red-hot needles and the fateful call from London obstinately refused to materialize. I was so nervous I could have crawled up the wall. Toward morning my wife took pity on me.

"You know what?" she said to me in a weak voice. "Maybe you ought to try a shower after all."

I had nothing to lose. I undressed and turned on the hot water (cold water is no good for spellbinding) and soaped myself thoroughly. After a while I reached my back.

London.

Seems I am an outstanding medium. Occasionally I switch over to the active side of the process. It may happen to me at any time, especially during the summer months. Suddenly I feel an irresistible urge to phone someone without any real reason. I pick up the mesmeric instrument and hot shivers run up and down my spine.

"Is Shaike at home?"

"Yes, but he's taking a shower."

Telephokinetics. The hot shivers start the moment Shaike begins to soap his back. This is the most shocking part of it: The contact is not created by the shower itself and in most cases not by the general soaping. Only the back is relevant. I made no end of experiments on the subject. A thick layer of suds on the legs—silence. The back—*trr, trr.*

I related my experience in an intimate circle of friends and many confirmed my findings. It seems that the moment a genuine medium enters the shower somewhere, all over the world people get up from their chairs and, without being able to explain their strange behavior, start dialing.

This writer is beyond doubt the country's last telepathic medium. I thought of submitting myself to a thorough examination, but I am afraid they would have me certified. As it is, there are enough scoffers. Only yesterday I had a phone call from one of the people doubting soap telepathy, a young physics lecturer.

"My dear sir," the fellow taunted me, "for your

information, for the past fifteen minutes I have been soaping my back in the shower and there is no ring!"

"Is the water hot?"

"Scalding, sir! And I changed the soap twice."

"Maybe the phone is out of order," I tried lamely.

"It is in perfect working order," the lecturer mocked, and added, "so where is your telepathy?"

"I don't know," I answered, brokenhearted, wiped the suds off the receiver and returned to the shower.

❧ *Because of our country's religious character, or, to be more precise, because of the lively participation of the religious parties in the coalition government, only traditional weddings may be held here, luxurious affairs with impressive rabbinical ceremonies and a rich buffet to serve the myriads of starving guests. This is one of those dearly paid-for pleasures. As a rule it is the father of the bride who covers the expenses of the Jewish wedding, in lieu of the dowry, and then flees to Belgium, leaving behind piles of unpaid bills. The divorce ceremony is infinitely more modest and inexpensive, but according to the statutes the wedding comes first.*

The Wedding Guests

We were tickled pink as we entered the hall where Amnon and Tamar were getting married. For weeks before the wedding we had racked our brains over what to buy the young couple. We had no intention of giving them a flower vase, since that would have been a little hackneyed. Therefore we spared no time and effort combing the gift shops until we found something very cute: a beautiful vase, perhaps a somewhat commonplace object, but that's all we found—what the heck. We placed our gift on the table bearing all the wedding presents. It was guarded only by a dreamy-eyed kid, and as none of the celebrants were looking, we wrote our name in big letters on the parcel we had brought, as well as on another, a fairly large box lying next to it.

The hall was one of the most beautiful in Tel Aviv, elaborately ornate, the tables loaded with goodies, while in a far corner a combo was in full swing. We were happy that our friends were entering holy matrimony in such auspicious circumstances and in such a posh place. This would surely engrave itself in their memories and help them through the difficult days ahead. The couple's other friends, too, were in an excellent mood. It was obvious that Amnon and Tamar's feast was their feast as well, though a number of the bride's friends, such as raven-haired Lilly, were not yet married and therefore had to be counted perforce among the spinsters. Senior citizens among the acquaintances even shed a tear or two on the sly and were not at all ashamed, because, after all, how many times in a lifetime does a person get married? Twice, three times as a rule, only seldom more often. But such statistics were quite irrelevant where Amnon and Tamar were concerned. It was the consensus of the guests that they were like a pair of cooing doves.

"A love marriage," stated Gusti, the bride's former boyfriend. "It's nice to find that romance still exists in this cruel world."

Lilly warmly concurred: They were literally crazy about each other. Tamar's parents had at first opposed the marriage. After all, she was their only child; they wanted somebody from abroad for her and all sorts of things. But Tamar simply said, "It's either him or you'll see what I'll do." So they had no choice but to agree. After all, the boy was making heaps of money, and the financial situation of Tamar's parents was not too rosy.

Look! Tamar has arrived. She is a dream. The slender girl in a snow-white dress looks like a professional model. Around her head there shines the halo of innocent love. Yes, there is something pure about this girl, something touchingly naïve. We all feel it.

"How beautiful you are!" Clarice calls to her.

Lilly cannot restrain herself and hugs her. "You are wonderful!"

Clarice was ready to swear that the bridal gown had been designed by Fischer. After the wedding Tamar would cut off a few inches and turn it into a smashing cocktail dress. At least I£20 the meter ($4.85; 1I£ = $.2425). French silk, apparently. But when should a girl wear a dress that had cost her a fortune if not at her nuptials? Especially after what the poor thing had gone through.

"Don't ask me," Lilly whispered. "You would not believe what this girl has been through! Her parents did everything in their power to have her marry that basketball player before she was called up in the Army. Everything was ready, but at the last moment a terrible hitch occurred."

"You don't say," we said. "Really?"

"But this is strictly between us. Exactly a week before the wedding one of poor Tamar's so-called friends went to the basketball player. You know those friends who love you so much but in fact never stop slandering you. Anyway, she served up a lot of filth about Tamar to the basketball player, but of course he didn't believe a word of it and only asked Tamar whether this was true. So she said to him, 'If you believe that this could be true, you are not a man and we'd better break it off.' The boy wanted to commit suicide, tried to hang himself, but because of basketball he was too tall—his head almost reached the ceiling—so he couldn't. Poor Tamar hit the bottle. He wanted to turn over a new leaf, but she said, 'Too late, Joseph!' I think they were still terribly in love with each other, but by then she had had an affair with an Army captain and then was passed from hand to hand. She really deserves some peace and quiet."

In the meantime the bridegroom had arrived wearing a dark suit. A handsome, tanned fellow with a pleasant face, very nice.

"Isn't he younger than she is?" Gusti asked, but the other guests quickly shouted him down. It was at most a matter of a few years. What does it matter? Tamar was still very good-looking and had studied beauty care. What really bothered us was this: What was her Amnon doing for a living? What was he actually doing all day long?

"Nothing," a gentleman with a pipe said. "He's getting married."

"You know him?"

"You bet I do. He's a good-for-nothing. I'm convinced even his suit is rented."

"The poor thing," we commiserated with Tamar. "What will they live on?"

"Don't worry. He'll work for her father," the man with the pipe scoffed. "He'll loaf around the office."

Well, yes, that's the fashion now. We seethed with indignation. Here was a good-for-nothing who could hardly count to three, but he was not ashamed of panhandling his father-in-law. Our glances followed poor Tamar's poor father. He was standing next to the rabbi, drafting the marriage contract. Looked like a shotgun wedding, really. The father seemed quite agitated. What could the reason be?

"A typical *nouveau riche*," Gusti whispered. "Made a pile of money in textiles and now he's buying his daughter a hubby."

Just behind us somebody was relating some juicy details about the old man's business deals. He was always fighting with his partner, so one day the partner disappeared under mysterious circumstances. The police even investigated. It is said they discovered shocking things, but what does all this matter now? The main thing is that Mr. Nouveau Riche has found this nincompoop for poor Tamar. Good luck to him. Anyway, he must be a terrible skinflint. You call this a hall? Couldn't he find something more decent in the whole of Tel Aviv? Just look at those tables: a few limp sandwiches, pickled herrings, mayonnaise salad and orange juice. Amnon and Tamar surely deserved better than this. They look so lovely together, don't they?

"Tamar looks tired," Lilly allowed in a worried voice. "She's taken on the mannerisms of an old maid. I tell you, people ought to marry their first love!"

'She's happy and that's all that matters," Clarice defended her friend, "though I've told her a million times not to put light-toned powder on her nose, because that makes the plastic surgery stand out."

"What?" We crowded around her. "What did you say?"

"You mean you can't see it? It's terrible! The doctor ought to be in jail, I'm telling you."

The guests are now grouped round the bridal canopy. Good-for-Nothing's mom and dad are all aquiver with excitement. They embrace the Nouveau Riches without saying anything, however. Strange. It's said that they are not too happy about the match; they would have liked something better for their son. Just between you and me and the door post one can't blame them either. But Good-for-Nothing had put a *fait accompli* before them.

"As a matter of fact," the man with the pipe asked quietly, "why did they have to hurry so much with the wedding?"

"Why indeed?"

This was a very naïve question. A knowing smile played around the guests' lips.

"Look," said Gusti. "Now it can be told. After all, the whole city knows it. Last winter Amnon ran away from home. His parents hired a detective. They were found dead drunk in a Jaffa tavern. Tamar's brother wanted to kill him. The police radio car was alerted. It was a pretty kettle of fish. Her father took an oath that he would shoot him down like a rabid dog if ever again he dared to come near his daughter."

Amnon walked up to Tamar and stroked her hair tenderly. Then he exchanged a few words with her.

"Okay," Tamar replied. "As you wish, darling."

You see, they are already fighting. It was really sad. Already. She had no choice, apparently. It was her last chance. She is no longer twenty, but a ripe twenty-two, so she had better keep quiet. The ceremony is starting. Good-for-Nothing stands rigid like a statue. He's as pale as a sheet! I think Tamar is cross-eyed. Lilly whispered in my ear that she always wears glasses, so now she is blind as a bat, the poor thing.

The bridegroom's parents are now standing right next to the bride. A beautiful ceremony. Good-for-Nothing is putting a ring on her finger, a very modest ring, considering his vast income.

"Where are they going to spend their honeymoon?"

"They've spent it already."

"What's the difference?" Pipe scoffs. "This time it's Daddy Kirshner who'll pay the hotel bill."

We drew his attention to the fact that the name of Tamar's father was not Kirshner. Then we found that he—Pipe, that is—was here by mistake. He had meant to go to a different wedding. But since he had come, he had stayed. Amnon broke the glass with his heel. According to some spectators he did it with barely disguised fury. In a corner somebody was laughing hysterically. Everybody looked in her direction. That's yet another story. People inform me that that broad had gone steady with Good-for-Nothing for two years, but then she had got into hot water and had suddenly married a foreign diplomat. They had carried on as if nothing had happened, but then Good-for-Nothing had discovered that the diplomat had known about him all along and was very upset. Then they began meeting again, whereupon Tamar's father had threatened him with a pistol.

"When's he going to betray her?"

That question had been in all our minds right from the beginning. It was inevitable that somebody would ask it eventually.

"Personally," Pipe said, "I give them three months on the outside."

Gusti bet a week.

Lilly was even more pessimistic. "Tamar is not as silly as she seems," she whispered. "Last night she said to him, 'Amnon, I am marrying you in cold blood. I'd rather be a divorced woman than a spinster.' So help me, she is right."

The apartment is registered in her name. Clarice mentioned in passing that she knew a very good lawyer, just in case.

"We'll see," the guests mumbled. "You never can tell."

We looked at those two young monsters. They try to get married. Kiss each other lovingly, pretend, but their cruel fate is obvious to all onlookers. The ceremony is finished. We hurry over to the newlyweds and smother them with good wishes and loving kisses.

"*Mazel Tov! Mazel Tov!*"

"Much happiness and joy in life."

"Till a hundred and twenty!"

"*Tfoo . . . Tfoo . . . Tfoo . . .*"

❧ And now the immediate consequence of premature marriage: the pink, cuddly baby one would like to hug and smother with kisses to stop its howling. We are specifically referring to our brand-new daughter, Ranana, the first baby fitted with stereophonic crying.

Pacification

Ranana is already past her second birthday, but she is still addicted to pacifiers. Our doctor says this is quite normal; all babies suck pacifiers in the transition period between breast feeding and the onset of the smoking habit. He says that the pacifier serves as a mother substitute, though as a rule mothers are not made of pink plastic with a yellow rubber nipple in the middle. Anyway, this is a perfectly legitimate symptom, and the only thing that keeps us awake at night is the fact that our Ranana is not fond of pacifiers as such but loves only one by the name of Tsetsy.

Tsetsy, which rhymes with Betsy.

To the adult eye Tsetsy is an ordinary pacifier, a mass product of the infant-oriented industry. But our ginger-haired offspring refuses point-blank to touch any other specimen.

"Tsetsy," she yells until loss of consciousness. "Tsetsy! Tsetsy!"

Naturally, after the first "Tsetsy!" the entire family is already down on all fours, and the feverish search continues in a doomsday mood. Finding Tsetsy is for us as meaningful as was the cry of "Land!" in its time to Columbus, because after Tsetsy is found Ranana calms down instantly and sucks contentedly while we sprawl all around her, exhausted.

"It's a sign," our doctor says, "that the child feels herself deprived of parental love."

That's a lie, because we love her very much, at least as long as she does not yell. It all depends on Tsetsy. With Tsetsy about all is smooth sailing; without Tsetsy it's a bad trip. If we go out for an evening the wife gets the shivers whenever the telephone rings, since she is afraid it is the babysitter announcing she can't find Tsetsy and Ranana is already purple in the face. In such emergencies we hurry home at traffic-ticket speed over the bodies of cops and find the half-crazed babysitter burrowing in the debris of armchairs and couches, looking for the fugitive Tsetsy.

"Goodness," the wife sighs from time to time, "should Tsetsy ever get lost for good . . ."

That is a contingency we bar from our thoughts like the idea of a nuclear holocaust. And what is most maddening: How does Ranana know that Tsetsy is Tsetsy?

One early afternoon I slunk out of the house with the holy pacifier and made straight for the pharmacy where we had purchased it. I asked for the same thing from the same sales lady, in the same color, the same size, even the same year of manufacture, since I believed that just as in the case of wines there might be good and bad vintage years. The lady gave me a perfect copy. I put it in the same pocket and went home the same way.

The step-pacifier arched through the air.

"This isn't Tsetsy!"

The wife thinks it's the rot that makes the difference. And indeed, Tsetsy's rubber part has become—pardon the expression—somewhat green with use, which conceivably could add to the bouquet. In connection with this, I won't forget for years the pharmacist's face when I asked her for used pacifiers. We had no choice but to age a few in an improvised home laboratory, and with that in mind we bought some hydrochloric acid and other chemicals, dipped a dozen test pacifiers in the mixture and kept them there until the rubber parts greened like Charles Reich's America, but they stayed quite unsuckable. Ranana immediately discovered our trickery and yelled her head off.

"The solution," our doctor decided, "is tranquilizer drops."

He prescribed a large bottle of tranquilizers, but it was of no use at all. The other week we were sitting in the middle of the sixth row at the National Opera. The chorus had just started singing when the chief usher came up the aisle and whispered into the darkness, "Pst, pst, pacifier! Pacifier!"

We knew at once that Grandma had phoned. On the way out we trod on a few spectators and at home found the old lady in a state of collapse. It seems that Tsetsy had disappeared without a trace from the special nail on which we take care to hang it every morning.

"Tsetsy!" the distracted mother screamed. "Somebody's stolen it!"

Our first suspicion fell on the milkman, who had come in that morning to ask how many bottles we'd need for the holidays.

The wife telephoned him in the middle of the night. "Eliezer," she shouted into the receiver, "did you take the pacifier this morning?"

"No," Eliezer replied, "I don't take pacifiers."

"It was hanging on the nail and now it's gone."

"I didn't see it," answered Eliezer. "So it will be twenty-three bottles on Wednesday."

Clearly, he was trying to change the subject. The wife was thinking of alerting a telepathist and asking him to bring along his parapsychology and locate Tsetsy in the milkman's cowshed when the precious object was suddenly discovered among the springs of an upturned couch.

"How did it ever get there?" The wife raised her tortured face heavenward. "How?"

We asked our plumber whether there was a Geiger counter or something of the sort with which one could locate lost pacifiers. One of our neighbors, who for some reason had suffered a great deal from chronic sleeplessness, suggested we buy one of those dogs trained to locate hashish. We also heard that pilots are equipped with secret minitransmitters which start broadcasting after bail-out: *"blip, blip!"* But how could we attach a transmitter to Tsetsy?

The most logical solution would have been to tie Tsetsy with chains to the child's cot. But our doctor disapproved. "The child could strangle herself," he said. "Give her more love."

"Ephraim," the wife notified me, "I feel I'm going out of my mind."

She woke up nights screaming because of her recurring nightmare in which a pterodactyl flew in through the kitchen window, snatched Tsetsy and disappeared in the darkness of the rain forest. How would this poor woman ever find it when she doesn't even know how to pronounce ptero—what's its name? Besides, the little one was suffering lately from delusions in which it seemed to her that the pacifier was escaping by itself, as in the TV cartoons, hop-hop-hop and Tsetsy was over the fence.

Horrors!

In the end we did discover Tsetsy's terrible secret.

It happened on a moonless night. At first everything went according to plan: At exactly seven o'clock my wife and my mother-in-law walked up to the steel safe we had bought a week before. Each of them inserted a key, opened the safe and took out Tsetsy. Then they put the pacifier in Ranana's mouth as she lay in her cot and closed the door. By then we had insured the pacifier for I£20,000, but that was not much good since no amount of money can replace a beloved pacifier.

I got up and peeked through the keyhole.

"Woman," I whispered. "Come here quickly!"

Through the keyhole we saw Ranana's little figure quietly climbing down from the cot, then going over to the sofa and pushing Tsetsy into the upholstery. Then she crawled back and opened up with nonstop bawling. All of us were greatly relieved. So the child was quite sane, free of any complexes. She was not in love with her pacifier; she was simply and methodically torturing us within the framework of an improvised family circus. According to the doctor, this is quite a common phenomenon among mammals, probably caused by a lack of parental love. He prescribed another bottle of tranquilizers, but it was quite useless around our house. It no longer has any effect on the wife and myself.

This century's most important discovery is neither the atom nor the face of the moon but the universally accepted, ghastly realization that fat is disgusting. Our Jewish grandfathers and grandmothers were overweight to such an extent that they could hardly get into their pants and bras. They died at a hundred and three without realizing what an unhealthy way of life they were leading and that science was predicting for them a bitter end or something. Ask your family doctor.

Kohlrabi

"Ephraim," the wife asked me one day, "am I fat?"

"No, woman," I answered, "you are not fat."

"But you are fat."

"In that case, so are you—and how!"

As a matter of fact, neither of us is obese in the literal sense of the word. The little woman is perhaps a little rounded out at the edges, and I bulge slightly in profile, but this is more a personal feeling than the verdict of the scales. In any case, we registered with one of the weight-watching outfits, since that's what's with-it nowadays. My wife's pals tell marvelous stories about those associations which put an end to the easy life of heavy people, of how they trimmed down a well-known hairdresser from 130 (287 pounds; 1 kilogram = 2.2046 pounds) to 40 kgs. (88 pounds) in two months, of how a theater manager dropped from 90 kg. to 0 and vanished altogether.

At the branch office we were received by a manageress and an emaciated lecturer.

"Only three months ago he used to give up his bus seat to two old ladies at a time," dozens of his awed disciples related. "Nowadays he dances ballet."

The lecturer introduced us without further ado to the basic tenets: A personal file is opened for every weight-watcher; for a modest fee he receives a weekly oral brainwashing and a foreign-made printed menu. You don't have to stop eating, only to give up your sense of taste. Bread, fats, noodles, fried horrors—out! No cereals, carbohydrates—no starches, if you please! On the other hand, lots of kohlrabi, as much as you fancy, with no limitations. And cabbage. And two glasses of milk a day. Plenty of fish. Sports are out because they whet your appetite. Best of all: Sprawl on the floor and drink lukewarm water once a week. On the seventh day they weigh you at the branch office and if you haven't lost any weight, you ought to be ashamed of yourself. Those who have are chucked under the chin.

"That's very good," I said. "We're a little timid."

The manageress took us into a corner and weighed us in without shoes but with our keys.

'Sorry," the manageress said. "You don't have the required overweight . . ."

Everything went black before our eyes. We would have never believed that for such purely formal reasons we would be robbed of our elementary right to join the family of watchers. Actually, I lacked three kilos to become a certified fatso; she a bare one and a half, though she is built on the small side. So we went home and started eating everything that was forbidden according to the formula. A fortnight later we plodded back to the branch office, fully confident of having earned our admission. What is more, I stuffed I£50 in small change into my pockets.

"Welcome," the manageress said. "Now I can open a file for you."

The lecturer gave us his instructions: "Three big meals a day! Don't starve yourselves! Diversify! If you get fed up with cabbage, switch over to cauliflower! And the main thing, no starches! See you in a week's time."

We went home and kept the commandments for seven days and seven nights. Our cheese was white and lean, our bread green with cucumber. Then we weighed in at the institute and flushed with shame because we had gained 200 grams, without a coin in our pockets.

"That happens," the manageress remarked. "Be stricter with yourselves."

That week we consumed only kohlrabi, brought to our house in railway cars straight from the station. Indeed, we didn't gain any weight. The process had been arrested. The hand of the small scales we had purchased for home use stood in the same place all the time. To tell the truth we were somewhat disappointed. Seems that other watchers as well have had a similar experience. The body won't cooperate, refuses to consider calories. What does one do in such cases?

"I skip a meal a day," a veteran disclosed. "At lunchtime I go to the diplomats' restaurant and by the time they serve me it is dinner."

"I," a plump lady confessed, "go to the swimming pool and lose weight by immersion. At least for a few minutes I am happy."

The little one discovered an old pharmacy in Jaffa where the scales are out of order, but half the women in Tel Aviv are queued up there. And in any case, truth always comes out at the branch office. Our weights had become stuck for good. I looked at the little one, puzzled. Really, how come she wasn't losing weight? As far as I was concerned there was an explanation of sorts: A rumor had come to my ears according to which I was stuffing myself night after night with underground fats in the kitchen.

Yes, this was the vengeance of the kohlrabi.

In the seventh week of our ordeal, the most critical by all accounts, I suddenly awoke to the mad thought that I was dying to smell the sweet aroma of sizzling fat, that I had to fry something right away or else I'd go out of my mind. I would have been ready to kill for a few calories; the very sound of the words "cream puffs" caused a strange weakness in my knees. My dreams were under the sign of starch! I visualized it as a lovely girl dressed in a white bridal gown running over a field, with her blond hair streaming in the wind.

"Starch!" I shouted after her in Russian. "Starch, wait for me, *ya te lubliu*, Starch . . ."

That night I caught up with her. I slid off my bed, slunk into the kitchen and in a towering rage poured a whole pan of popcorn into a pot of boiling oil. I topped the white mountain with an outlandish amount of butter and gulped it all down—carbohydrates, starch, starch, starch. That was the start of the calorie festival.

At midnight I was standing in front of the stove, frying pears, when the fragile figure of my wife appeared in the doorway. With her eyes closed she walked straight to the laundry basket and, with an unwavering hand, took out of it about a dozen bars of chocolate. She started peeling off the foil and with a conspiratorial gesture let me take a bite. We devoured the lot, grunting like animals.

At the last moment my life instinct awoke. I crawled to the telephone and with my remaining strength dialed the branch office.

"Come quickly. We are eating. Chocolate."

"Hold fast!" the duty lecturer shouted. "We're on our way!"

The car drew up with shrieking brakes. They broke down the door and found us wallowing, drunk, among the foil. They saved altogether one and a half bars; the rest had swelled us beyond recognition.

The lecturer seated us on his knees. "Never mind, children," he said quietly. "This happens quite often to our members. They gain back in a few hours all they had lost over a number of years. So we start again."

"Rabbi," we implored, "no kohlrabi."

"Then let it be lettuce."

We dropped out of the ranks of the weight-watchers because we were utter failures.

I again bulge somewhat in profile, and the little one is rounded out at the edges, and so what? The stout fellow has a pleasant disposition. He is more generous and less excitable, because it takes such a lot of time for his anger to spread through all that adipose tissue, nor is he aggressive since he can't run. He is all smiles and jowls.

So get fat, folks, get fat. Stop starving yourselves and throw out all that rotten kohlrabi.

❧ *In the technocratic reality of our days, in which sophisticated machines and refined computers can manufacture anything under the sun without a single human hand touching the mass product, there are left in our country only a very few genuine craftsmen continuing the proud tradition of past centuries. Gradually even they, these last dinosaurs, are disappearing from our lives, and more the pity that their demise cannot be expedited. Do you, kind reader, sadly miss the dinosaur? I don't.*

The Last of the Craftsmen

One evening last week the wife looked at me as I was about to go out and said, "Why don't you have a briefcase to carry your papers in, like any self-respecting person?"

"So help me, you are right, woman," I answered. "My status as wielder of the pen certainly demands this."

"Go," the wife said, "and buy something special."

I went to the corner leather store and explained to the shopkeeper that I was looking for a special leather briefcase, something very impressive, black with a dull finish and lots of compartments, shiny locks and things. The shopkeeper was a little man who spoke only Yiddish and was not blessed with particularly good taste.

"A briefcase is a briefcase and not a jewel," he declared. "I can give you, sir, only what I've got, a very strong briefcase for I£25. If you want all sorts of gewgaws go and find yourself some artisan who's still got patience to talk to clients."

I was deeply insulted. Yes, I wanted first-class craftsmanship, but to say that I was looking for gewgaws? Woe to Jewish craftsmanship if this was one of its representatives. I left the Levantine merchant to his designs and went to look for a leather artist who had learned his craft in a civilized part of Europe. After a week's frantic searching I was lucky to locate Sigmund Wasserperl, the famous fancy leather-goods maker.

As soon as I entered the workshop I could smell the sharp fragrance of cleanliness and order. Next to a large worktable I spotted a pleasant blue-eyed and white-maned oldster. It was Mr. Wasserperl in person. I described my delicate situation—naturally in Goethe's and Chancellor Brandt's language—and he listened attentively. Then the respected artist informed me that for humanitarian reasons he was ready to undertake the job and would do his best to impart to the product a character befitting my status as fellow artist. What's more, so as to allay my doubts as to his professional ability, Mr. Wasserperl described to me in detail his past life, starting with his graduation from the Stuttgart Government High School and including the fateful moment when it came to him like a flash of lightning that his life would be completely devoid of meaning unless he learned to make fancy leather goods. At first Mr. Wasserperl apprenticed himself with the Singer and Singer firm in Hamburg, then he moved to the famous Viennese firm of Kirschner Lederwaren and worked there—in his words—for thirty-four fruitful years.

I chatted with Mr. Wasserperl until about midnight. In the end we remembered that as a matter of fact I had come about a briefcase, and the craftsman calculated the dimensions of my future briefcase with a slide rule and logarithmic tables. Then we went on to discuss the leather meeting the demands of outer perfection and resistance to torque.

"What's your opinion on burnished buffalo hide?" Mr. Wasserperl asked.

"That's it," I answered. "I like that. Let it be burnished by all means."

"I'm really happy," Mr. Wasserperl breathed, greatly relieved. "It's a very strong hide which suits itself particularly well to ornamental embossing."

By then my initial enthusiasm had dampened somewhat. Also, I had not eaten for six hours.

"I don't want any gewgaws, you know." I tried to bring the old man back to earth, but Mr. Wasserperl interrupted me with an impatient wave of his hand.

"No second-rate workmanship is done here," he flared up. "My thirty-four years with the firm of Kirschner Lederwaren place a heavy responsibility on me. All I'm asking for is a little patience. Your briefcase will be ready day after tomorrow and the price is I£30."

Two days later I went to collect the briefcase, but it was not yet ready. What's more, Mr. Wasserperl had not even started working, because during two sleepless nights he had come to the decision that buffalo hide would, after all, not be suitable since it was a little too porous and he would better use gazelle or zebu hide, which were perhaps a little more expensive; on the other hand they should last 100 to 150 years. Then and there I agreed to hammered zebu hide and we parted.

Three days later I came to collect my briefcase but learned from Mrs. Wasserperl that the old man had traveled early in the week to a fine mechanics factory to order the special round-headed studs made of hardened brass with which he intended to fasten the fringes of the briefcase. I told her I didn't want any studs—life was too short for that; we have to enjoy every minute of it—whereupon Mrs. Wasserperl retorted that her husband belonged to a vanishing breed of craftsmen who would rather stop working altogether than give out a poor product, not like those Israeli quacks. She took the opportunity of reminding me that her husband had worked for thirty-four years for the firm of Kirschner Lederwaren, who were court purveyors to His Majesty Emperor Franz Josef of the House of Hapsburg.

Gradually I resigned myself to the thought that I would end my life as a writer without portfolio. But one misty morning Mr. Wasserperl showed up in our apartment. The old man looked alarmingly tired and worried and complained bitterly that at his age he had to scour the country for a few stupid studs, while in Vienna such accessories could be found in every shop. The artist's very appearance was a mute accusation of humanity as a whole and for a while I thought I could hear the wings of fate beating ominously. As a matter of fact, Mr. Wasserperl had come to talk about the lining of the briefcase. He thought that only stained unicorn hide would do in view of the extraordinary resistance to wear of this rare material.

"My dear Mr. Wasserperl," I said to him, "I really appreciate your professional standards—after all, thirty-four years with Kirschner Lederwaren are not to be sneezed at—but so help me, I really don't need such a unique briefcase. Knowing my little wife, before long I'll be bringing vegetables home in it."

The old man's face lighted up. "I am glad you warned me. If so, we'll have to see to it that the briefcase is waterproof both inside and out. Under the circumstances I'll line the briefcase with sheared sealskin.

Have you, sir, got some relations in Canada?"

"Listen, Wasserperl," I said, "a briefcase is a brief-case and not a jewel! Why don't you just finish the bloody thing and be done with it?"

"I simply can't," the deeply injured craftsman flared up. "Do you think it's easy for me? And, since you mentioned it, how do you think, sir, that I could satisfy all your whims for I£30? Who will compensate me for all the time I'm wasting on this?"

Then I noticed that the poor old guy had become a nervous wreck; his face was twitching and he resembled nothing so much as a dried prune. I dispatched an urgent cable to my Uncle Egon in America and asked him to airmail me a whole sealskin. A fortnight later I cleared the parcel through customs. I hurried with the skin to Mr. Wasserperl. To my great satisfaction the old man was in a good mood, since during a quick trip to the Negev he had purchased from a couple of Bed-ouin shepherds some jute rope twine interwoven with gold braid with which he intended to fashion the brief-case straps. But when the old man noticed Uncle Egon's parcel he blanched and his knees started knocking.

"Plastic!" the old artist whispered, unspeakable dis-gust on his face. "They dare to bring plastic to Was-serperl!"

The craftsman tossed the material into the garbage bin, walked to the cupboard and without saying another word took out an antique hunting rifle. Then he threw a scornful glance at me and stomped out of the work-shop. His wife shouted desperately after him, but he went on, head erect and straight-backed until his tragic figure was swallowed up in the noon darkness.

"He is now going to hunt in the desert." The woman broke into bitter sobs. "I know him. He can't work otherwise. That's one of the reasons why they liked him so much at Kirschner Lederwaren."

"Thirty-four years," I reminisced, somewhat shaken, but my sincere sympathy only poured salt on Mrs. Wasserperl's wounds.

The old woman fell on me. "Why do you torture my husband? Do you want to kill him for your silly briefcase?"

"Yes," I said. "One of these days I'll kill him."

During those troublesome days I seriously entertained the idea of knocking him off because I too had worn myself out in the struggle for the briefcase. But on that Tuesday I got a message which shook me to the depths of my soul: Mr. Wasserperl had been hospitalized in a critical condition. Afflicted with deep pangs of conscience, I bought a big bunch of flowers, put it in my new briefcase, which I had bought for I£25 from the Levantine shopkeeper, and went to visit my victim. At the hospital I learned that somewhere on the Red Sea coast Mr. Wasserperl had shot the close relation of a seal, but the rainy weather and the exertions of the trip had overtaxed his strength and he had arrived home burning with fever. His wife was now sitting next to his sickbed and the two of them looked at me accusingly. Mr. Wasserperl was as yellow as a piece of old parchment and his eyes were bloodshot. He motioned me to bend over him. I pressed my ear against his mouth.

"You'll have . . . to find . . . silver clasps . . ." the old man whispered. "I won't agree to copper clasps. They are not suitable."

"Yes, Granddad," I whispered back. "I'm listening."

"Also," he continued with his last strength, "you'll have to get some swan dung. It's the best thing for burnishing leather."

"Everything," I promised. "I'll do everything, Granddad. I'll devote my remaining years to our brief-case, only you get well quickly."

The old man spoke no more and sank back on his pillow, completely exhausted. Full of remorse, I hurried to the head physician, with Mrs. Wasserperl's tearful curses speeding me through the hallway. The doctor explained to me that he could do nothing at present. All the patient's wishes must be fulfilled to raise his spirits. Because—that's what the doctor had learned from a reliable source—Mr. Wasserperl had been with a certain firm in Vienna and he would rather die than do a shoddy job. I asked him to pass the hospital bills on to me. Tomorrow I am going up to the northern swamps to see about swan dung. I am still young and able to work.

🌣 *Only two years ago if someone asked us what was the secret of our little country, how was it able to withstand so many enemies, what made Israel's youth so conscientious, we answered in all sincerity that the secret was that we had no TV. Well, for the past two years we have had TV and our children, too, are now spending a large part of their lives in the darkness, like young, half-blind bats, groping for food crumbs in the dust, while their eyes search for their father on the little screen. Woe to the father who does not show up there. And woe to him if he does.*

The Watershed

Before the turning point my life had been one of drab anonymity.

Only rarely did I succeed in earning a modicum of public recognition—for instance, when I wrote the monumental new Hebrew Encyclopedia, which got special mention in a women's magazine, in the "Books Received" section, namely: "E. Kish. Hebr. Enc. 24 volumes." Then, if memory serves me, on one of my summer vacations I conquered Kilimanjaro, and had the Reuters correspondent not caught the flu I would certainly have been mentioned on the radio. A few years later I succeeded in composing Beethoven's Tenth Symphony, and then at long last a moderately favorable review appeared in the "Fun and Games" section of a Yiddish weekly. Another bright moment in my life: After I discovered the cure for cancer, I was received by the Minister of Health and we chatted for about fifteen minutes, until the arrival of the delegation from Uruguay. Anything else? Yes, lately I devoted myself to history and wrote the great epic of the Jewish People from the Patriarch Abraham to Pinhas Sapir, a 4,000-page work, and was interviewed on the radio. But as far as the man in the street was concerned, I was a nobody.

And then the great turning point arrived.

As a matter of fact, it happened right out of the blue on that fateful Tuesday. A kid walked up to me on the street with a microphone in his hand and asked me what I thought of the situation. I answered, "It's gonna be all right."

Then I went home and forgot all about it. But at dinnertime there suddenly came a marrow-chilling shriek from the living room, where the children were having their meals on the rug in front of the TV set. My son Amir appeared in the doorway shaking in every limb.

"Daddy," he gurgled, "Daddy . . . on TV . . . Daddy . . . TV . . . Daddy . . ."

The child was quite hysterical. We called the doctor and soon we heard him shout as he bounded up the stairs, "I saw you!" he roared. "I saw . . . it's gonna be all right . . . TV! . . ."

Then I remembered that, indeed, another kid had stood there with some sort of camera while they asked me my view on things in general. The telephone started ringing.

"Thank you," an old lady from Jerusalem wheezed into the receiver. "Thank you on behalf of mankind."

The first bunch of flowers was sent by the Knesset Speaker. "I was deeply moved by your uninhibited and optimistic approach," he wrote. "I wish you success in all your endeavors." He also asked for two autographs. Then the neighbors filed in and lined up along the walls, gaping at me for hours. The more daring among them drew near, touched the fringe of my coat, then withdrew, overcome with emotion. During the early evening hours an engineer from the Haifa Technion arrived to check my profile.

"Just as I thought," he said and winked at me. "It's gonna be all right, hey?"

These were days of glorious madness, a marvelous time, when all the dreams of youth came true. As I passed places of public gathering, people would whisper behind my back, making a sound like a beehive at election time.

"Look, there he goes, the guy from Tuesday."

In more than one store it happened that the sales lady stared at me with saucer eyes, blanched and dropped in a dead faint. Women, who until now had been totally indifferent toward me, suddenly got a glint in their eye. And flowers, flowers, flowers. To tell the truth, even the wife's attitude toward me changed for the better. One moonless night I awoke and found her leaning over my prostrate form, looking at me as if she were seeing me for the first time.

"Ephraim," the woman whispered. "From the side you resemble Ringo Starr."

Even personally I changed a great deal.

My steps became more masculine, my appearance more impressive. According to my mother, I have grown by two or three centimeters. I became accustomed to beginning my sentences as follows: "As one who appeared on TV only a few weeks ago, I think . . ."

After all these years of frustration and failure, of mucking around with stupid encyclopedias, symphonies and epics, it was only natural that I should become intoxicated with the sweet taste of instant success. According to a conservative estimate, I was seen on Tuesday by all the country's inhabitants except for one Shlomo Milstein. That nonconformist inhabitant had missed me because a fuse had blown just as I came on. I reconstructed the interview for his benefit in a personal letter. It is reasonable to assume that our street will be renamed "Interview Street" or "Appearance Avenue" or something of the sort.

Anyway, I had a new set of calling cards printed:

EPHRAIM KISHON

as seen on National TV
"It's gonna be all right"
23 Heshvan 5529

I need such calling cards badly during these cold evenings, because the ungrateful crowds seem to be forgetting me. This has come as a rude shock. Lately, it happens quite often that people look right through me, as if I were an ordinary writer and not one who has been shown. I inquired in Jerusalem whether a rerun was planned to jolt memories, but no.

And they had to postpone commercial TV!

I hang around places where the kids are shooting TV shorts, but no luck. Once I sat at the opera and they came straight toward me, but at the last moment they shot someone who was picking his nose. I started picking as well, but it was too late.

I'm desperate. Day before yesterday they informed me that I had won the Bialik Prize. I asked whether there would be TV coverage; they said no. I did not bother to go. A charwoman at the TV studio promised to slip me among the extras in the new series "What's Your Trick?" Until then I'll be just another drab unknown, shrinking and disappearing, until I'm no more.

❧ *According to reliable statistics the most pitiless wars always took place against a religious background, because one can forgive anything of his fellow man except that he pray to his creator in a style different from one's own. In our country, since there is no genuine competition from any other faith, the dispute rages en famille between the camp of the observant who observe Moses' precepts to the letter, as written down in the minutes of the Sinai meeting, and the American Reform Movement, which takes into consideration that in the meantime the world had been given the electric refrigerator, Karl Marx and homogenized milk, to say nothing of Mexican divorces.*

The Yecch Affair

One of these stormy evenings, while still greatly upset by an unbridled attack on Reform Judaism in the Knesset, we got the idea of consulting one of the main personalities involved in the affair. We knew beforehand that it was not going to be an easy interview in view of the delicate subject matter, yet it should be interesting to learn the official thinking on the *kulturkampf* we apparently cannot avoid.

I: What is Your opinion on the essential difference between the two main trends in Jewry?

THE LORD (*somewhat apologetically*): Unfortunately, I have been kept busy lately with a problem of a quite different nature: The force of gravity is decreasing in space, the universe started expanding and there is a danger that one of these days the infinite will end and I'll have to start everything from scratch. How far away are you from the sun?

I: In Jewish or Arab numerals?

THE LORD (*impatiently*): Arab, of course.

I: 153,000,000 kilometers.

THE LORD: So within less than a billion years you'll be more than two hundred million kilometers away and who knows what will happen then? (*Officiously*) Please remember that your earth is but a minor planet in the solar system, and there are millions of solar systems in every galaxy.

I: When the rabbi of the Sanhedria quarter in Jerusalem heard a Reform service he said, "Yecch!" and spat twice!

THE LORD: Of galaxies with billions of celestial bodies I've got at least several millions, so you must understand that my attention is somewhat divided between the venerable rabbi and the rest of my problems.

HIS VIEWS SHOULD BE ASCERTAINED WITHOUT MIDDLE MEN

THE LORD, brilliant, urbane and world-famous, is responsible for creating the universe a billion years before Christ. In 3000 B.C.E. he developed, launched and peopled the earth, all in a matter of six days, and ever since he has been catering to its needs with no small success. The interview was conducted in idiomatic Hebrew, interspersed here and there with Hungarian expressions.

I: Lord, we believe that You, more than anyone else, are interested in a strict observance of the Commandments.

THE LORD (*categorically*): May I ask you not to try and ascertain my views through middle men.

45

I: Are You religious?

THE LORD (*somewhat hesitatingly*): No. At first I felt a certain affinity toward their cause, but nowadays, I'm sick and tired of it. (*Sharply*) You down there think of every position, of every little politico, but never of me! My situation up here is simply untenable. On the one hand they credit me with the giant works I have set up, with the superhuman laws which keep nature ticking along marvelously and which are quite beyond human understanding. On the other hand they expect me to listen every morning to the same story and the same Byzantine praise which they heap on me as if I were some sort of artist starved for applause. (*Quotes from document*) "Great King, Hero of Heroes, Ruler of Generations, Unveiler of the Hidden, You who are praised by all, Life-giver, You who Remember the Forgotten. Whose eyes are wide open, Holy and Awful, in Parable and in Fear," and so on hour after nauseating hour. Now really.

IT WON'T WORK IN THE LONG RUN

I: Lord, they praise You out of a deep feeling of respect.

THE LORD: I beg your pardon. This is an insult to my intelligence! Does the Creator of the World need such transparent flattery? You wouldn't have dared to feed such stuff to the computer of the Tel Aviv Municipality! (*In a calmer mood*) So help me, my boy, it's time to ease up on me a little. A few changes here, a few cuts there won't hurt anybody. Otherwise it won't work in the long run. (*Shrewdly*) Really, how can you ask today in Golda's Golden Age that men and women should not pray together? And I don't ever remember having said anything about head coverings and certainly did not mean any medieval Polish furs. (*Puzzled*) Did I ask you to walk in kaftans in the summer heat? Am I your enemy? You are simply trying to alienate youth from me.

I: It's tradition, Lord, Your tradition.

THE LORD: Don't rely on me in everything, will you? (*Pointedly*) For quite a while now you have been traveling to the moon, and yet you have the temerity to declare that I, you hear, that I have forbidden public transportation on the Sabbath! I, whose every move spells logic! Or take your marriage ceremony which is still conducted in Aramaic, a language even I don't understand. (*Checks himself*) All right, I don't want you to misunderstand me. I haven't got anything against the religious, as long as they don't force me to think the way they do, but I ask you, why do they have to say "yecch!" every time they mention the Gentiles in their prayers or elsewhere? How does spitting fit in with the fact that I personally am in charge, not only of them, but of the whole Universe, including the star and zodiac worshippers on Mars? The whole World is yecch? Now is that what we set up the State for?

YOU MUST MAKE ALLOWANCES

I: Are You an unbeliever, Lord?

THE LORD (*categorically*): Absolutely not! Please make this quite clear! (*Slowly*) I am simply trying to protect my status among mankind against the machinations of the fanatic parties. They expect me to demand in all earnest the strict observance of all 613 of the commandments, as if nothing had happened in the meantime. Try for once to look at things from my point of view, for God's sake . . .

I: Lord, do You belong to the Reform movement?

THE LORD (*cautiously*): I don't want to commit myself at this stage. Let's say I sympathize with them. The main thing is that I am a Jew.

I: With all due respect, where is Your proof?

THE LORD (*surprised*): You are right. No one ever legally defined who is a Jewish God. (*Pensively*) I am a Jew because I am a Jew. (*Warmly*) You see, I like you all, I am full of goodwill, but you must make allowances. Please don't alienate me from religion. Make it possible for me to carry on my office in the coming generations as well.

I: Thank You, Lord. May I tell our readers that You still consider us Your chosen people?

THE LORD (*cordially*): Certainly. I like you more than the other peoples.

I: Why?

THE LORD: You are so funny.

In the beginning there was gasoline and the exhaust pipe, then were created the engine and the car, the horn and the traffic light. To these were added the parking meter, traffic signs and the traffic cop, and in the end Satan climbed out of the big city's sewer and changed Hell's name to "parking lot."

Following is a Biblical version of the story.

One Hell of a Job

There was a man in the city of Tel Aviv whose name was Job Kunstatter; and that man was perfect and upright, and one that feared the law, and eschewed evil.

And there were born unto him seven sons and he had a pickup truck.

And that man was the most virtuous of his generation, and he drove most cautiously on the roads and highways, and he went to and fro in the country and walked up and down in it, and never once was he laid hand on by traffic cops and given a ticket. Also Job paid his municipal taxes before they were due, and furthermore he was alone in his generation who did thus.

Now there was a day when the sons of the Municipality came to present themselves before the Mayor, and Satan came also among them.

And the Mayor said unto Satan, "Hast thou considered my servant Kunstatter? There is none like him in the city, a perfect and an upright man, one that feareth the laws and escheweth evil."

Then Satan answered the Mayor and said, "Hast not thou made a hedge about him all his life? But put forth thine hand now, and touch all that he hath, and he will curse thee to thy face."

And Satan and the Mayor then and there made a wager. And the Mayor said unto Satan, "Behold, all that he hath is in thy power; only upon himself put not forth thine hand." So Satan went forth from the presence of the Mayor and that is how it all started.

It came to pass one morning that Job Kunstatter rose from his bed and went down into his yard and black darkness fell on his eyes and he staggered. That is because the man always parked his truck in the yard at night, as it was difficult to find parking space in the busy street. But on that morning a behemoth of a truck stood in the gate of the yard and blocked the way to him. Job shouted and honked and also went and asked the neighbors about the owner of the truck, but he found not his identity until 10:30 A.M., when the man came with measured steps and it was Eliphaz the Parker.

"Man," Job lifted up a cry. "Dost thou not see that this is a gate to the yard?"

"I see nothing," quoth the truck driver. "I make parking where I want."

And he went forth and parked likewise on the morrow and on Thursday. Job's eyes knew no sleep at night from fear that he might arise in the morning and find the exit blocked before his pickup truck, because only with it could he earn his bread. Then he got up at dead of night and went down in the street to look and even put slips of paper on the truck of Eliphaz the Parker which read, "I warn thee for the last time, thou swine, that thou shalt stop parking in front of the gate." Nor helped this at all, for Eliphaz was much bigger than he and—his body had waxen fat on him. Job became a nervous wreck, but in all this he sinned not, nor charged the Mayor foolishly. He went to the police and lodged a complaint against Eliphaz the Parker.

"We cannot do anything," they told him at the police, "as long as there are no official signs before the entrance to thy yard."

"If so," quoth Job, "I shall observe the words of the Prophet."

For thus said Jeremiah, "Set up signs," and Job did not spare time and effort to attain his goal. He hurried to the Road Marking Department of the Municipality and submitted an application which was rejected out of hand and Job submitted an appeal and again pleaded and was again sent packing and came back and would not give up.

"Shall we receive good at the hand of the authorities and shall we not receive evil?" he asked and did not rest, until one day two inspectors rolled into his courtyard and found that the place was pleasant in their eyes for parking purposes and approved his application, and barely two years later two proud signs were standing at the two sides of the entrance, viz: "Five yards. Entrance to courtyard," and on the other side, "End of restriction."

And there was great rejoicing and his sons made a feast unto their friends and were merry with wine all night and Kunstatter rose very early and went out into the courtyard and black darkness fell on his eyes, for the gate was again blocked to the pickup truck. A great shout arose from Job's mouth and he ran straight to the cop on his beat.

"I know, sir, I know," the cop calmed him. "I have already written out a ticket for the offender."

That is to say, it seems that in the meantime cars had multiplied so bountifully in the crowded city, until the citizens had no choice but to park on every empty space, even at the risk of a ten-shekel fine for not obeying the signs.

"This is worth my while," Eliphaz the Parker once informed Job. "Though it costs me a few shekels every moon, I have not to search for parking space in the dust."

And not only he but also others went on to park in front of the courtyard between the signs and Job rent his mantle and shaved his head and fell down upon the ground, and worshipped.

"The righteous suffer," he shouted, "and the wicked rejoice."

Then a cloud of dust fell on the courtyard and Job's wife stepped out of it.

"Why dost thou lie there and weep?" the woman asked. "I shall tell thee what thou must do. Simply put thine own pickup between the signs at night and no one else shall take away thy place."

And Job did as he was told, and after many moons of heartbreak and nights of unrest, sleep again returned to his eyes. And the man rose early with joy in his heart and went down into his courtyard and black darkness fell on his eyes because on the windshield of his pickup truck was glued a life-size ticket.

Job ran to the cop on his beat and foamed, "Why didst thou write me a ticket, oh, cop?"

The cop pointed at the signs.

"What is written there, sir? 'No Parking,' yes?"

Job sounded his famous laughter. "Ha ha. They set up those signs for me, that I may come out of my courtyard with my pickup in the morning."

"Go out then, sir," said the cop, "but stand not thy car where parking is forbidden!"

"But it is forbidden for me!"

"Of course for thee and for everybody else too, sir."

"Dost thou not understand? This is *my* sign."

"Then thou must serve as an example to others, sir."

And on the morrow there was again a ticket on the windshield, and Job sprinkled dust upon his head and shouted, "Why signs if there be no redemption in them? If I park in the courtyard, they block me. If I park outside, they ticket me. Let the day perish wherein I was born."

In those days Job Kunstatter no longer did anything but deal with sign matters, and his face dropped and his steps faltered. He spent half his life between the walls of the various departments trying to have justice done.

"The police must impose fines according to regulations," they explained to him. "It is not written on the signs that the place belongs to thee."

But Job answered and said, "If so, write it there!"

"Oh, no," the authorities said. "Only diplomats and well-known politicians are entitled to reserved parking places in the street. An ordinary mortal like thee can get at best free entrance to his courtyard. By the way, why shouldst thou park outside when there is room in thy courtyard?"

After this, Job opened his mouth and cursed all those present and he was kicked out and marked a callous wrongdoer and his fingerprints were taken. And he removed the tickets every morning and did not pay a penny and was hauled into court and found guilty and his calamity was very great and his family was troubled lest one night he die. And one morning he went down into the street and lo and behold there was no trace of his pickup truck between the signs, because the patience of the police had run out and they had towed it away to a place of haven so that it should not obstruct the entrance to the yard.

Thereupon Kunstatter's nerves snapped and he said, "Is my strength the strength of stones? Or is my flesh of brass? Until when will I be afflicted by traffic cops?"

His sons became fed up and scattered unto the four corners of the world and his wife packed her bags.

"Dost thou still retain thine integrity?" his wife said unto him. "Dost thou not see that the signs are ruining thee? Have them removed and thou will be able to park in front of thy house without being fined."

Then Job hurried to the Municipality and fell down in the dust before the Traffic Commission and beseeched it to remove from his head the visitation of the signs.

"And what dost thou think this is—the marketplace or the palace of authority?" the officials flared. "Only yesterday or the day before thou pressed us relentlessly to install signs in front of thy yard."

"That was long ago," Job answered. "Hidden are the ways of traffic in our city, amen."

The authorities dropped a sympathetic tear.

"The heart weeps for thee but our hands are tied," they said. "Because it is not thou that wast given the signs but the parking place in thy yard, and as long as the yard stands, there must be free access to it."

"I shall go forth," Job stuttered, "and destroy the yard. I shall blow it up. I shall scatter anti-tank obstacles all over it."

He was kicked out bodily from all commissions and did not know rest to the end of his days.

As a matter of fact Satan, whose idea, it will be remembered, the little game had been, had long ago won his wager and things simply rolled on by themselves. One moonless night the cop on his beat noticed a dark figure using a big saw on a street sign, and before Job could complete his task he was arrested by the cop and hauled before the judge. For five months Kunstatter sat in a dark hole of a prison and the curses never ceased flowing from his mouth, so much so that his jailers stopped their ears with moss.

It is said that on his release Job found that his pickup truck had been stolen, but not even this redeeming news could cure his sick spirits, and his tracks vanished into the wilderness. According to legend he still wanders around in the southern desert, and tourists relate that sometimes his eerie laughter is to be heard in the distance and he is seen running along the skyline sounding a car horn 140 times.

❧ *The number of parking spaces is limited by the physical size of the globe. In our country the situation is particularly severe, because a well-known law of physics states that the smaller the country, the larger and wider its cars. It happens quite frequently in our cities that the 1973-model American car is found to be wider than the 1714-model street. In such cases the street parks in the car. Even in the big parking garages the situation is catastrophic because once the much tried Israeli car owner at long last finds a parking space, he absolutely refuses ever to relinquish it. What's more, the garages themselves sell tickets for half an hour, half a day, a full day, and eternity.*

The only solution for the little man is to cut his vehicle in two—that is, to return to the trusty old motorcycle. For a fairly long period in our life we were the happy owner of such a two-wheeled marvel, until one stormy night we parted from it in strange circumstances.

The Hitchhiker

On that Saturday night I left Petach Tikva homeward-bound in the saddle of my motorcycle. On the outskirts of the city I noticed a shriveled old man waving his hands desperately and croaking at the top of his voice, "Tel Aviv, Tel Aviv." My Jewish heart awoke in my breast. "One of these days you too will be old and shriveled," my heart whispered, "and you too will be glad if some nasty young chap gives you a ride on the outskirts of Petach Tikva." I pulled up at the curb, brakes shrieking, and motioned the old man to hop on.

He clambered up laboriously.

"There are some decent people left after all," he wheezed in fluent Yiddish. "May heaven bless you, sir. Let's go!"

I don't like to be worshipped. All I had done was to fulfill my duty to a fellow human being in the spirit of the United Nations charter—that was all. I turned around.

"Hold on tight, Granddad. Everything will be O.K.!"

"*Oy*," the poor fellow groaned. "This saddle is stuffed with rocks."

He was right. The rear saddle was without springs, that's a fact. I was a little ashamed of riding in such comfort while this patriarch was being tossed about like a cork on a stormy sea. Besides, he had to hold onto his hat with one hand. Most unpleasant, really.

"I hate motorcycles," the old man remarked. "They are so noisy and smelly. You from Tel Aviv?"

"Yes."

"Then how come you don't have a car? Every spiv in Tel Aviv has a car."

"If it's so uncomfortable, Granddad, you can get off right here."

"Now? In this darkness? In the middle of nowhere? You've got very funny ideas, sir, I must say. Couldn't you drive a little faster?"

I shot forward.

"What a terrible wind there is on this cycle!" the oldster complained. "You'll be the death of me yet. But what do you care? You won't visit me in hospital, I'm sure."

I'll visit you, I vowed mutely, so help me I'll visit you. Granddad clung to my back like his counterpart in

Sinbad the Sailor. I was moved after all. Poor Grand-dad. Goodness knows what he had gone through before he became so embittered.

"You are a very poor driver, you hear," my passenger remarked. "I wonder why they allow the likes of you on the road. Such things happen only here. Any rowdy who takes it in his mind to drive a cycle gets a permit. And then people ask themselves why there are so many accidents on the road. How many people have you run over so far?"

"I've been driving for ten years now," I reassured him, "without a single accident, thank—"

Boom!

The rear tire blew and we found ourselves in the ditch. The engine sputtered on for a while, then died. The oldster got up sighing, groaning and cursing.

"Murderer!" he shouted. "I knew it from the start! Speeds like a madman."

I examined my passenger carefully. As a matter of fact, he wasn't that old. He was a squat, thickset man. Predictably the tire had burst under his weight.

"Now look at me," he said. "Here I am in the mid-dle of the night, broken and injured, but what can one expect from a Jew who travels on the Sabbath?"

"I am so sorry, sir. I didn't do it on purpose, be-lieve me."

"Who cares? My neighbor dropped an iron on her baby's head. She didn't do it on purpose either, but the child is now an idiot for life."

I saw I would have to change tactics. Getzl—that's what I had instinctively named him—sat down on the curb. I asked him to get up and help me drag the mo-torcycle to a nearby street lamp, but Getzl replied that he was no porter. I informed him that unless he helped me I would leave him out there in the wilderness.

"I see," Getzl shouted. "Blackmail, hey?"

Cursing freely, he took hold of the forward fork. From time to time he stumbled and let fly a few remarks in Polish. I told him, "Go on, curse me as much as you like. I don't understand Polish, but don't you dare curse my mother because she understands that language a little." We set up the motorcycle in the light. I had another good look at my passenger. A well-built, healthy man, my age, maybe a few years younger. For a while we stood there staring at each other with remarkable lack of sympathy.

"Listen!" Getzl suddenly exclaimed. "I know you from somewhere. Didn't you work last winter in Kirschbaum's butcher shop?"

"Who, me?"

"Yes, you! You thought I wouldn't recognize you? I had to stay in bed two days after they threw that frozen chicken at me."

"Frozen chicken?"

"Exactly. It was you, wasn't it?"

"Yes."

A real pleasure. The sudden success encouraged me to continue.

"And if you ever again dare show your mug in the shop," I added, "I'll throw a frozen turkey at you."

"Why?"

"For the sake of law and order."

Getzl was completely confused. I made him work harder than he ever had in his life. He had to hold up the mud guards, and once when I caught him off his guard I asked him to hold the chain as well, a job which soils a person's hands even more than embezzling public monies.

"Are you threatening me?" Getzl wheezed, lavishly covering himself with grease. "I'll see to it that the Petach Tikva police take an interest in you! Do you know Inspector Goldblatt?"

"Of course. He's my brother."

That just about finished Getzl. He mumbled that he would get even with me yet. At the same time he kept waving at the cars whizzing by. Yes, it would have been a real treat for him to leave me there with a sick motorcycle and ride to Tel Aviv in style. Naturally, not a single car bothered to stop, the Lord be praised. An ugly temptation took hold of me: A light shove and Getzl would find himself under the wheels of the speeding cars. No, I won't have him work behind my back! I gripped the monkey wrench more firmly. While I inflated the wheel, Getzl watched me with burning eyes.

"Hey, you think we'll ever leave here?"

"If I feel like it."

He waved listlessly at a black Chrysler. Like hell it will stop! But what do you know? A miracle! The Chrysler did stop. I burst into the big car as if a horde of creditors were chasing me. "Drive!" I shouted at the driver, and we took off. The motorcycle was lost, but Getzl was stuck with it in the moonlight. Life is beautiful. Very beautiful.

🌷 *Whatever one may say of Israel, it has terrific sex appeal. Otherwise one could not explain its dizzying success with tourists. It frequently happens that a couple of tourists from Buffalo, whose living-room windows open on the mighty cataract of the Niagara, are overwhelmed with emotion at the sight of our national water carrier in which the water drops—drops, I said? No, trickles—down from a height of seven feet. Sex appeal—that's what we have. Especially in our famous spa, Eilat, where the tourist miracle takes on Biblical proportions.*

A Seaful of Miracles

We have been in Eilat only once, quite a long time ago. Though our stay was brief, we exhausted practically all the rich opportunities for entertainment offered by this unforgettable place. We visited King Solomon's pillars, bathed in the Red Sea, took a brief nap, then, greatly refreshed, dashed down to Solomon's columns, inspected the columns, swam a few strokes and squeezed in a trip to the columns.

But all this is not a patch on that great international attraction, the glass-bottomed boat. That world-famous frigate enables you to view in comfort all the wonders of the deep blue.

It is related that quite a few tourists have come down to Eilat planning to stay a day, rashly boarded the boat and are now incurably addicted to it.

Small wonder then if we also succumbed to the lure and bought a ride on it. Our fellow travelers were a Canadian millionaire with his wife and a couple of lovers. The navigation company provided the appropriate romantic atmosphere. The seats had been left in the innocent, rough-hewn state, and the glass bottom had not been scrubbed for ages. The captain was an old sea dog.

We put to sea without a hitch. As if a magic wand had been passed over it, the bottom suddenly spread out under us, flat, without a ripple, with each grain of sand scintillating in the green opaqueness of the sea.

For about thirty minutes we drifted over it, and the wonderful sand never once changed its texture. Never before had we seen sand so faultless, so uniform, so devoid of discordant features, only smooth sand, continuous sand, exclusively sand. Grunting ecstatically, the Canadian millionaire took pictures.

"There!" the millionairess shouted and pointed a shaking finger downward. "There!"

We looked down and our heart almost stopped beating. On the undulating bottom, in the blinking twilight, we made out a dark form partially covered with seaweed. No doubt about it; it was a huge bus tire spreading a mysterious calm all around it.

We continued our dreamlike trip. The young couple pointed, giggling, at the yellow-tinted rocks gliding by underneath. The Canadian remarked that he had seen many rocks in a life of globetrotting, but never such uniform ones as these.

Strewn among the rocks were all the treasures of the Arabian Nights: a wide assortment of bottles, empty and full, round and square, broken and whole, some of them filled with colored sand of the kind sold to the shore-bound tourists.

It was as if Jules Verne's fabulous story-worlds had come alive before our amazed eyes. We practically stopped breathing with the excitement of it all. Unexpectedly, something moved.

"Fish!" I screamed. "Fish!"

The old man of the sea again cut the engine, so that we might better enjoy the unforgettable sight.

Practically under our feet, three sardines flashed by in a flurry of glittering fins, then disappeared among the cracks.

The old seaman announced, "Gentlemen, there is a sunken ship right under us."

We bowed deeply over the glass bottom, afraid to miss anything of the majestic sight. At first we could not make out anything in the murkiness, but slowly our eyes became accustomed to it and we saw that we could really not distinguish anything at all.

"The sand has covered it completely," the sea dog explained in a choked voice, and in our mind's eye we saw the frightful tragedy taking its inexorable course in the depths of the cruel sea. The young lady began to tremble and begged to be taken back.

"All right," the millionaire agreed, "but I must see the Kent once more!"

The captain veered to starboard at a sharp angle and set out for the open sea at full throttle. After a mad chase of about half a minute, we stopped. The millionaire dropped flat on his face and shouted rapturously, "Kent! Kent!"

At the foot of a rock there appeared a virginally white and whole cigarette box. Only one side of it had been opened. The inscription was still legible; only the "nt" had become covered with some kind of fungus. The millionaire took a few low-angle shots of the box, then we returned to base.

If I forget thee, O, Eilat, may my right hand lose its cunning.

❦   *"He who laughs last laughs longest," says the well-known proverb, hinting at those idiots who get the point of the joke only two hours after the telling. For a world condemned to perpetual warfare, this stupid proverb is anyway pointless, because simply no one laughs longest. One side develops a new missile, and six months later the competitor has an anti-missile missile, whereupon the first party quickly comes out with an anti-anti-missile missile, and so on until bankruptcy. As for ourselves, we are perfecting the technique of endless warfare by peaceful means: income tax.*

Looping the Loophole

Some time ago Zalman Weintraub, the noted matzoh baker from Jerusalem, commissioned a solemn toast from me, which he, Mr. Weintraub, would reel off in response to warm greetings his admirers and employees were to deliver as a surprise at the jubilee party. Weintraub offered me for the spontaneous toast a writer's fee of $230, in three equal installments, and I, needless to say, was overjoyed at the windfall. However, after applying some elementary arithmetic, I found that the effort was not worthwhile, since I would have to travel twice to Jerusalem in my car, and the fuel would cost more than was left out of the fee after all taxes and tolls were deducted.

"You'll have to find some arrangement," the little wife opined. "Go and see Spielberger."

Spielberger is the best tax adviser in town, a shrewd expert familiar with every loophole in the existing laws, since he himself had drafted them when he was still head of the Treasury's Investigation Department. He listened with knitted brows.

"The question, sir," he said at the end of my report, "is, do you earn more than a hundred and ten dollars a month?"

"I'm afraid I do."

"Don't you by any chance plan to leave the country? Emigrants get certain exemptions."

"No. I'm staying."

"Then it is a difficult situation," the expert concluded. "Couldn't you go to Jerusalem by taxi?"

"No, I couldn't," I explained. "I get sick in those big cars."

"Sit next to the driver."

"I can't take the risk. At the last moment some pregnant woman might show up and take my seat."

Two days later we met again.

"There are two possible solutions," the expert informed me. "The first is rather simple: Your wife will have to buy a company with registered losses and serve as your literary agent."

"Fine," I said. "We'll shop around for one."

"Just a sec," said Spielberger. "It is a *sine qua non* that you personally may not be involved in the company in any form whatsoever, since she is representing you. Are you by any chance getting divorced?"

"Not yet."

"Never mind, we'll manage somehow. Your wife's company will get your whole fee from Jerusalem and not pay tax on it, since this sum will only diminish the company's losses."

"Marvelous idea!"

"Wait! Now the money is registered with your

wife's company, but the problem is: How to get it out of there? If your wife simply withdraws the money from the company as her fee, she'll have to pay tax on it."

"Oy."

"There is a way out. Your wife's company will have to set up a subsidiary in your son's name, and she'll take out a life insurance for you in the amount of the writer's fee you'll receive from Mr. Weintraub. As you know, life-insurance premiums are tax-exempt."

"Do I have to die?"

"That would be the ideal solution, but it isn't a must. There is a certain kind of insurance called 'the living dead' which makes it possible to cancel the policy after three years and get a refund in cash."

"Wonderful!"

"But," the expert continued, "there is the danger that the authorities might consider this 'a fictitious deal'; therefore it would be desirable to make the beneficiary a third party who has no formal ties to you or to the subsidiary named after your son. Have you a friend you can trust?"

"No."

"Then I'm willing to serve as your third party. In a separate agreement between us I'll declare myself a trust fund for the purpose of the insurance premium so that I'll have to place at your disposal the insurance payments which will be refunded to me at the end of the three-year period."

"You are a genius!"

"Wait! You'll have to pay full income tax on every pound."

"Oh?"

"So I'll pay you through libeling."

"I beg your pardon?"

"Since last summer this is the only possibility of effecting payments between two permanent residents. According to the laws in force, and at least for the time being, you don't have to pay tax on damages for libel awarded to you by a regular court."

"Why not?"

"Because it's accepted as an expense."

"Splendid!"

"Thank you. Only two months ago I transferred five hundred dollars to a contractor. True, this necessitated my slapping his face twice, but in your case a bit of invective will do. For instance, we'll say that you've got a Hungarian accent."

"That's not libel," I said. "I've really got a slight accent."

"In three years' time it might be gone."

"I can't trust in miracles."

"We'll find a way out. What matters is that you should sue me for libel and the damages awarded should exactly cover the refunded insurance payments which your son's subsidiary will effectuate in my favor as a trust fund in the amount of the writer's fee, which Mr. Weintraub will pay into the losses of your wife's company. Do you approve of the idea?"

"Sounds all right," I had to admit. "But you said something about a second solution."

"Yes," stated Spielberger. "Don't give a receipt and don't declare anything."

"That's out. I don't want complications."

🌱 *Every people fights the tax burden according to its national character. Thus, the Italians simply stop working and acquire a healthy tan at the beach. The Americans squander tax-exempt donations and leak their philanthropy to the press, while the English rob trains and do not declare the loot. The Israeli solution is the most sportsmanlike.*

Squaring the Ball

It may be safely stated that though the government's economic policy has not boosted productivity all along the line, it has proved itself completely successful in at least one field: in the football pool, whose country-wide output closely approaches that of the national lottery. Naturally, there is a world of difference between the two institutions. While the lottery is based on plain stupid luck, the pool is a test of a person's skill in the sports, since the little player must give proof of above-average familiarity with the workings of the National League. The procedure is very simple: You buy a form at one of the pool counters and in the throes of Messianic clairvoyance forecast the results of next Saturday's games. You write "1" or "2" next to the winning team, or "X" for a draw, then on Saturday leave the radio on all day, note with deep satisfaction that you have twelve correct guesses and win I£162,530,000.

"Go," the wife said. "Make a bundle at the pools."

This sounds easy enough, but it should be pointed out that personally we are not much of an expert at football. What's more, we avoid the game on principle because the seat we paid for is always occupied by a burly fellow in a striped polo shirt, and if we point out to him that he is trespassing, he drawls, "So what!" and ripples his biceps. In view of these circumstances we appealed to Uri, who never misses a match, and requested his help in filling out our form. Uri literally outdid himself in his perceptive analysis of the odds.

"The new forward of 'Joy in Work' Sodom sprained his ankle last week against Haifa," he mused, "so I'd guess a draw against Maccabi-Jaffa. On the other hand, 'Joy in Work' Beersheba has a good chance of beating 'Blue and White' Jerusalem because they are better on a muddy field."

And so on. We wrote it all down, spellbound by Uri's know-how, handed in our form and waited impatiently for Saturday. Than we found that we had a single correct guess and even that was a writing error of mine. In other words we had wasted good money on that idiot. An Eilat housewife had scored twelve correct guesses. We complained bitterly about Uri.

"You are really silly," people informed us. "Every babe-in-arms knows that the experts never win at the pools."

We learned that there are a few proven methods for guessing, such as the size test, according to which the largest city always wins—that is, Tel Aviv beats Haifa, Haifa Tiberias, Tiberias Caesarea and Caesarea Givat Brenner Kibbutz. Then there is the home-ground method, according to which it is the team playing at home that always wins. But best of all is not to understand a damn thing about soccer. Wily old foxes, it is said, keep in hiding a person or two who has never even heard of the game (an old crone, a three-year child, an Israeli politician) and fill out the forms only according to their advice.

"Whoever understands even a little," well-informed people advised us, "is out."

I felt like bashing my head against the wall. What a glorious ignoramus I had been only a month ago! I hadn't known anything at all about football. I could easily have made twelve good guesses. But like a fool I studied the game by the sweat of my brow and nowadays I can no longer keep an open mind while writing down the 1–2–X. Let's face it, I'd lost my youthful innocence.

"So what are you waiting for?" the little one scolded me. "Let's look for some morons."

We started looking for fresh talent all over the neighborhood but found that by now all had been snapped up. In their feverish search for football innocents the wily old foxes had even hired an old Bedouin woman in the Sinai desert. The trouble was that the fresh moron guesses correctly once or twice, as long as he was completely untried, but then he too starts taking an interest in who won and who lost and quickly forfeits his ability to make off-the-cuff guesses.

Take Amir, for instance.

The idea occurred to my wife last month when a kid aged eight in a village near Jerusalem won I£131.517. We seated Amirele on his potty and I started reading out the games to him.

" 'Joy in Work' Judean Hills versus 'Joy in Work' Eilat. What's nicer?"

"Eli."

"Maccabi Sodom versus 'David's Sling' Haifa."

"Daddy."

That week we won I£172 with eight correct guesses. The following week Amir made us I£92. And then what do you think happened? The third week the young oracle suddenly called out, "Daddy, 'Samson' are champs, aren't they?"

In other words, by now he knew the ropes. They had spoiled him in kindergarten, I am sure. He made just three correct guesses.

"Nowadays you can't trust your own son," I lamented. "What shall we do now, woman?"

The little one's glance swept across the fence into the neighbor's yard. There was Jimmy, their outsized watch dog, scratching his belly. The method I worked out was simplicity itself: Jimmy lapped up the soup we had brewed him as bait and I queried him about the week's games. If he raised his head it was "1"; if he smacked his lips, "2"; no reaction, "X."

"Well," we said, "if this doesn't work nothing will."

We won I£524. Jimmy guessed all scores with computerlike precision, and he would surely have enriched us had not many others as well been exceptionally lucky that week. In any case we saw in Jimmy a unique opportunity for obtaining economic independence. My wife cooked him special soups; we even bought him choice tidbits.

"Two pounds of bones," the wife asked at the butcher's, "but big ones, please. It's for the pools."

And then what? Jimmy was stretched out in a trance next to the brimming plate, while I was registering his guesses, when I suddenly felt a shiver running down my spine.

"Woman," I whispered, "look!"

Yes, there was no doubt about it. Every time I said "Joy in Work" the dog pricked up his ears and crinkled his nose. He was beginning to get the hang of things. Everything was lost. Finished. We did not even submit the form. As of now we are going back to the lottery, where there is still some room for serious guesswork.

🌿 *The British solution to tax evasion—i.e., romantic robbery—has lately become so popular in this country that our most prestigious dailies are running a permanent column headed "The Weekly Robbery." This is due to the fact that the police and the rest of our young country's security forces are still at the stage of on-the-job training. You can't start out right away with the university of crime, can you? First you have to go through elementary school, or rather kindergarten.*

Mission Possible

Upon investigating a recent robbery which netted the thieves I£330,000 after taxes and which was carried out most skillfully against the money van of the veteran Israeli security company Nick & Carter, one has to start by stating unequivocally that the attack had come as a complete surprise to all concerned. First, at least ten days had passed since the previous robbery of the company's money van, and at the time only I£33,000 had been carried—to quite a different bank. Therefore, it could not have been foreseen that this could happen again.

Besides, Nick & Carter had taken special precautions this time and had not published its money-hauling plans in any daily newspaper. What's more, they had even waived the use of an armored car, so as not to attract the attention of potential robbers. All the company markings were removed from the sturdy van carrying the three tons of banknotes, and even the sign on the roof, "Beware! Money!" was covered with masking tape. Therefore, no one could possibly have foreseen hitches or anything like that.

True, about two hours before the security van left there was a telephone call to the offices of Nick & Carter.

"Excuse me," someone inquired, "are you moving money today?"

"Yes," the duty security officer answered, "to the postal bank."

"How much?"

"Three hundred and thirty thousand in cash. Who's speaking?"

"Wrong number."

The man at the other end replaced the receiver, and the duty officer, realizing that it had been a mistake, forgot the whole thing. But now the investigators are connecting the mysterious call with the "man on the tricycle." That is, while the I£330,000 was being loaded on the van out in the street, a man was sitting on a yellow tricycle parked somewhat to the side, jotting down the number of bags, as the money was packed in small handy bags for easy transfer to another vehicle in case of breakdown or something. After the bags were loaded, the man climbed atop his tricycle and from there started signaling with small flags in the general direction of the city, but he was taken for a sailor, and only much later, during the reconstruction of the robbery, was he remembered as a possible accomplice.

For the very same reason little attention was paid to the three men who took up position in the early hours of the day around the postal bank armed with Karl Gustav submachine guns and Katyushas of Chinese manufacture. They were taken for saboteurs or something. There was no policeman on the spot, Nick &

Carter having requested removal of anything that could have given warning of the impending money shipment. Only a lone plainclothesman showed up, and even he was of the robbers' party.

At the postal bank it was business as usual. True, about an hour after the doors opened a young book-keeper spotted an unknown man walking around the building and cutting the telephone wires with a pair of rusty pliers. At first the young bookkeeper took the man for a hippie or New Left, since his face was covered with a wool stocking, but when he climbed on a desk and started pulling out the safety fuses, the bookkeeper walked up to the man and asked him what was he doing there.

"I am from the post office," the man answered, and the young bookkeeper accepted this explanation. Only after a while did he remember that in fact they were the post office, whereupon he went to report to the Old Man, who, however, was at a meeting with Sulzbaum. In the meantime, ever more signs were pointing to the fact that something was brewing, especially after the man with the stocking pulled out a pistol and asked all those present to lie down on the floor. All obeyed, ex-cept for an old cashier who did not lose his presence of mind but moved his foot slowly toward the secret alarm button under the table. Alas, the button was secret and it could not be found. So he lay down on the floor as well and waited. A number of clients who walked in were surprised to see all the clerks lying on the floor, but most of them believed that this was for TV and joined the others in the hope of getting a spot or something.

Just then the robbers outside were emptying the security van. The two armed guards of the Nick & Carter Company could not actively resist, since all they had in the way of weapons were field howitzers, and even these were pointed from inside toward the van door, while the robbers happened to come from the side. One of the guards tried to coax the criminals. "Open the door. It will be worth your while," but they wouldn't listen and grabbed the three hundred and thirty thousand in cash. The other company guard, a more experienced man, returned the robbers tit for tat and quietly cursed them in Rumanian.

It should be mentioned that a taxi driver stopped nearby while the money was being transferred. He suspected something, went to a pay telephone and dialed 999 for the police. He kept dialing for about a quarter of an hour until the robbers finished the job and, passing the telephone booth, shouted to him, "They changed the number. Dial 1-0-0!"

But by then the driver had no tokens left, and at the post office they had run out of them five days previous, so the man drove to the Central Bus Station to buy tokens, but on the way there he switched lanes on a one-way street without signaling and was arrested by the police, fined three points and sent for a blood test. Later, after the paper came out with an illustrated report, a radio car was dispatched, but the cops could not find the street as there were no signs and drove to Jaffa instead and there set up a road block—that is, they hid behind a curve and waited for the robbers to come and park less than twelve meters from the bus stop. But the robbers got wind of the scheme and failed to show up.

The management of Nick & Carter announced that the robbers had not been as smart as they thought, since they had forgotten to take inflation into account. It also announced that in future their guards would be equipped with tear gas, making it easier for them to cry. There is also talk of installing a solid-steel safe for storing the money, the revolutionary invention of a young Israeli engineer.

The public is kindly requested to cooperate with the security forces. Should anyone spot unknown persons with stockings on their faces paying money out of bags marked National Bank of Israel or something, he should immediately call the police, 999. Thank you.

> Our subtropical country is permanently endangered by the hostile proximity of a hundred million Arabs, but the average Israeli citizen acquires his compulsory ulcers from the upstairs neighbors, who choose to water their bloody rubber plants just when he sticks his head out of the window to check whether it's going to rain. A long time ago Josephus Flavius immortalized this daily skirmishing in The Jewish War.
>
> In day-to-day practice there are hundreds of effective means of making a neighbor's life miserable and forcing him out of his apartment. To mention but a few: Twelve-inch woofer-tweetter loudspeakers, giant-size thoroughly rotten dustbins, early-morning piano practice by the open window. Following is a remarkable chapter in the story of bad neighborliness, copyright of the Association for the Prevention of Cruelty to Animals.

Aristobulos the Enforcer

At the other end of our suburb, right next to the highway, there is a small cluster of luxurious two-family villas framed by gardens. Until now we were convinced that this neighborhood was nothing less than paradise on earth, but after the Aristobulos affair we are no longer so sure.

What actually happened?

What happened was that in one of the villas there lived Opaz Mayer, music teacher, and Yehoshua Spiegel, clerk. The two men and their families immediately hit it off on the wrong foot and did their level best to remove each other from the common property. They emptied tons of garbage on each other's gardens, cut their antenna wire, and it is said that Opaz Mayer once even attempted to wire up Spiegel's bathtub to the high-tension line. The situation became even more critical when Yehoshua Spiegel realized that as long as Mrs. Spiegel worked his whole salary was being gobbled up by the Department of Internal Revenue; therefore he resigned, and ever since only the woman works, while he is at home all day long bursting with energy and re-pressed initiative. Indeed, it was obvious to everybody that one of the two neighbors would have to leave. The question was, whose nerves would snap first, and the betting was three to one in Opaz Mayer's favor.

So far this is a fairly routine story that could happen in any block of apartments where Jews live. But one cloudy day events took an historic turn. Namely, the Spiegels acquired a dog by the name of Aristobulos. He was not a big dog. On the contrary he was quite small, but his bark had all the characteristics necessary to drive an ordinary neighbor out of his mind, to say nothing of a neighbor who was also a music teacher with perfect hearing. Besides, Aristobulos always barked at the most inconvenient hours—that is, at 5:15 A.M., between 2:00 and 4:00 in the afternoon when Mr. Mayer was taking a nap on the sofa, and again at midnight and between 3:30 and 4:00 A.M.

On the third day of the dog's appearance in the arena, during the regular afternoon concert, Mrs. Mayer came out into the garden and from there broadcast the following warning in the general direction of the Spie-gels' house: "Listen, curb that monster if you know what's good for you. Otherwise, so help me, my husband will shoot him!"

Nor was this an empty threat, because the whole neighborhood knew that Opaz Mayer kept a hunting rifle at home. Therefore Mrs. Spiegel took the warning to heart, and ever since, whenever Aristobulos started his non-stop barking, she immediately appealed to him in a soothing voice as follows: "Quiet, Aristobulos! You are disturbing Mr. Mayer. Aren't you ashamed of yourself? Quiet! Sh-sh-sh!"

But the dog did not quiet down. On the contrary he stepped up the decibels, as if trying to demonstrate his belief in the freedom of barking. So Mr. Mayer wrote his legal adviser and requested the protection of the law against this four-legged disaster, but strangely enough it appears that the lawyer took Aristobulos' side. He replied to Mr. Mayer that according to the law it was every citizen's right to keep a barking dog at home, and there was no clause in any law which defines the kind of bark or its timing.

What else could Mr. Mayer do?

He got up one moonless night, grabbed his rifle and set up an ambush behind a clump of trees, waiting for Aristobulos' inevitable exit. But the dog only barked at the customary hours (2:00; 3:30; 5:15) and did not come out. From time to time Mr. Mayer thought he heard the dog scratching at the door and whining disconsolately, but his masters did not open the door, partly out of cruelty, partly because they sensed the danger lurking out there.

The next two nights were exact replicas of the first. The dog barked and stayed indoors. But Mr. Mayer lost patience and sneaked up to the window of the Spiegels' bedroom to check into this physiological mystery. Opaz Mayer pressed his nose against the windowpane and looked—and could hardly believe his eyes.

What he saw was this: Mr. Spiegel lay on his bed, a bored expression on his face—and barked. Next to him Mrs. Spiegel dozed fitfully, repeating from time to time the following automatic message: "Quiet, Aristobulos! You don't let Mr. Mayer sleep. Quiet!"

Mr. Mayer's first impulse was to shoot the sonofabitch, but he then took hold of himself, went straight to the police and related the whole shocking story to the duty officer. The officer listened attentively, then awoke and asked, "So what?"

"Man!" Opaz Mayer roared. "That sonofabitch ruins my hearing and has not let me sleep a wink for a whole week!"

"Sorry," the officer answered. "I can only act against loudspeakers blaring after midnight. I cannot prevent anyone from barking, except if he does it while illegally pasting up posters. As a matter of fact, this comes within the jurisdiction of the municipality."

So Mr. Mayer went home and next morning, after Aristobulos had awakened him at 5:15, hurried to his lawyer and pleaded before him that Yehoshua Spiegel was keeping a self-dog in his house. The lawyer consulted his books and after a while gave his client a totally negative legal opinion.

"In the British mandatory law there is absolutely nothing which forbids the imitating of animal voices. What's more, Ottoman law even prescribes the fee to be paid a person employed as watch dog. So the only solution for us is to lodge a complaint against him because he has not applied for a permit to keep a dog in his house."

The astute lawyer was as good as his word. The very next morning he submitted a complaint against Yehoshua Spiegel for not paying the dog tax on himself and demanded the dog's immediate arrest. But he was informed then and there that he was badly mistaken, because the tax had indeed been paid for a whole year in advance on behalf of a pedigreed dog of Scandinavian breed by the name of Aristobulos the First.

In the meantime the barking grew louder by the hour; it was as if Aristobulos realized that this was the final battle.

Mr. Mayer made a last desperate effort and informed the Minister of Health that, judging by his voice, his neighbor Aristobulos was a rabid dog whose destruction in the public interest should not be delayed any longer. A government veterinarian was immediately dispatched to our neighborhood, gave Yehoshua Spiegel a thorough check-up, issued him a clean bill of health, and then the Ministry of Health debited Mr. Mayer with the expense of the examination.

That did it. Early this month the Mayers pulled up stakes and moved north. Since then this is again a quiet neighborhood. According to radical circles here, Mr. Mayer ought to have barked back. But naturally it is very easy to dispense advice but rather difficult to bark a duet.

"Man's best friend"—this ancient delusion is not spread by the dogs but by their masters at the other end of the leash, especially by those blessed with a fresh litter of give-away pups. In fact, truth must out, dogs simply cannot stand humans. They stick to them for dry existentialist considerations, along the lines of "half an hour's tail wagging in exchange for a generous per diem." We humans need dogs so that there should be someone around who loves us professionally and madly. That this is bought love? If so, it's not the only one of its kind.

One-Pupmanship

One evening not long ago my wife decided that the children wanted a dog. I categorically refused.

"Again?" I asked. "We discussed this before, didn't we?"

"Only on a trial basis," replied the woman, "for the children."

"Naturally. But afterward we'll get attached to it and won't be able to get rid of it."

The woman had a few talks with the children and as a result Amir and Ranana broke into wild sobs, viz: Daddydogdaddydogdaddydog. A certain compromise appeared on the horizon.

"O.K.," I said, "I'll buy a dog, Which kind?"

"Pure-bred," my wife said. "With a pedigree."

From this I understood that she had already consulted the neighbors who own the monsters making the neighborhood unsafe. And indeed now I remember for the last few days they had looked at me pityingly.

"I am not interested in a big dog that will turn the whole house upside down," my wife continued the briefing, "nor in a little dog. It is disgusting. I also heard that young dogs pee on the carpets and old dogs have asthma. So one has to be very careful about the pedigree. An anatomic body-build, straight legs, pigmented jaws and the main thing—straight hair. In short, what we need is an obedient dog with a sharp bark, but quiet, non-chewing, house-broken, and under no circumstances a bitch, because they are in heat twice a year. I also don't want a male dog because they chase the bitches, but a pure-bred dog whose ancestors were registered for several generations with a reputable veterinarian, because only these are worth the price one pays for them."

"All right," I said. "So this is the dog the children want?"

"Yes. Go and look around. But for God's sake don't buy the first dog they offer you."

So I went to town looking for action. On the way, out of habit, I went to the post office in order to buy a new postal-rates booklet and stood in line in front of a man with a severe cough. Apparently he noticed that I was worried because he asked me if I was looking for a dog. He said he had one just around the corner from the post office, in his garden. I went with him, and we found among the bushes in a used shoebox a pup with curly hair, bow legs and a black nose with a lot of pink spots. The dog was chewing on its own tail, and as soon as he spotted us he jumped up at me and licked my shoes with gusto. I became attached to him right away.

"What's his name?" I asked.

"Who knows?" Coughs answered. "You can have it."

"Is he pure-bred?"

"What do you mean pure-bred?" the man flared up. "This dog is made up of quite a few breeds, so for me he is very pure-bred. The main thing is he barks. Do you want him or don't you?"

I saw that he was angry, so I agreed. Also, as I said, I had become attached to the dog.

"How much do you want for him?"

"Nothing. Only take it away."

He wrapped up the pup in a newspaper, pushed it in my hands and shoved us out of the garden. But I had hardly gone two steps when I suddenly remembered my wife and drew up short. This—it flashed through my mind—this is not exactly the dog we had discussed only a few minutes ago. What's more, should I bring it back home, both of us would be kicked down the stairs. I looked inside the newspaper. He trembled slightly and only his head protruded from yesterday's news. Then I realized that as a matter of fact he had a pink nose with black spots. No, this wouldn't pass muster at home.

I hurried back to the coughing man.

"I'm not going home now," I lied. "I'll fetch him later on in the afternoon."

"Listen," the man puffed, "I'm ready to pay you a few pounds . . ."

"That won't be necessary. I've already become attached to him. I'll fetch him soon, don't worry."

"Well," the woman asked, "any luck?"

This was a very primitive trap, I must say.

"You don't buy a dog as quick as that," I said coolly. "I consulted several experts today and they offered me a few Scotch terriers and a rattler, but they were not pure-bred enough for me."

I was not quite sure whether a breed called "rattler"

really existed, but somehow it sounded credible. To tell the truth, I am not quite sure what "pedigree" means either. What is pedigree? A diploma? Front teeth? Inspector Pedigree?

Anyway, the wife saw that I was taking the dog-buying business very seriously. This calmed her. After all, the main thing was not to buy the first dog offered.

"No need to hurry," she remarked. "After all, how many times in a lifetime does one buy a dog?"

"Of course," I agreed. "I've seen a few ads in the newspaper. Tomorrow I'll go and make a few cautious inquiries."

Next day I went straight to the beach and frolicked about in the waves. I even played a few games of beach tennis with the lifeguard. At lunchtime, on the way home, I made a quick visit to my dog at the coughing man's and had fun with him for a few minutes in the garden. He was very happy to see me, the dog, and licked me all over, and then I noticed that even the topography of his tongue was very indistinct. This dog has not a single pigment of nobility in him, I sadly decided. How will I bring him home?

"Tomorrow," I said to Coughs, "tomorrow it's a sure thing. We are getting anti-rabies shots today, the whole family, and day after tomorrow we'll be safe."

"The ads in the paper are not worth the ink they are printed with," I related to the wife. "They are offering me all sorts of mongrels. That's not for me."

"Still," the woman asked, her inquisitive eyes sweeping my tense features, "what have you actually seen?"

She forgot that I am a poet of sorts.

"I have seen a Yorkshire poodle, not bad at all, in Ramat Gan," I told her dreamily, "but his pedigree reached back only four generations. Besides, I couldn't rid myself of the impression that several of his sisters and brothers were inbred."

"So what?" the wife retorted. "That's quite natural with dogs."

I raised my voice. "Not with me! With me the word 'pedigree' still has a precise meaning, if you don't mind. Either I find us an aristocrat, or else the hell with it."

The wife looked at me with new admiration in her eyes, the like of which I have never seen before.

"Maybe you are right," the little one whispered. "To tell the truth you surprise me pleasantly. I thought you'd bring home the first dog that crossed your path."

"You see?" I berated her, almost choking with fury, "we have been married for twelve years and you still don't know me! If you must know, I am driving to Haifa tomorrow morning to consult Dr. Manczel, the number-one expert on German shepherd dogs."

Next morning I took leave of my family and went straight to Max. So help me, he's a really nice dog. He literally jumped at my collar out of sheer exuberance when I entered the coughing man's garden on tiptoe. I intended to teach the dog some elementary rules of be-havior, such as jumping over hurdles, catching criminals and such things. But Max was quite unteachable, to the extent that for a few minutes I even regretted that I had become attached to him. To top it all, Coughs suddenly showed up and kicked up a row that he would toss the bloody bitch out of the garden if I didn't take her immediately and added a few sentences in Polish.

"Excuse me," I said to him, "did you say 'bitch' just now?"

"What's the difference? Take it away!"

Max looked at me with her sad eyes and her tail wagged her muscular body.

"Why?" her glance said. "Why aren't we going?"

"I'm working on it," I signaled to her reassuringly. "I'm working on it."

At home I dropped onto my couch completely exhausted from the strain of the long drive.

"I talked to Dr. Manczel," I summed up the situation. She showed me a number of fairly pure-bred dogs, but my instinct warned me not to fall into her trap."

"Aren't you exaggerating a bit?" the little one asked. "No one is perfect."

"I won't tolerate compromises," I shouted. "I decided, woman, to buy a thoroughly pure-bred dog from a famous Swiss kennel."

"How much is this going to cost?"

"Don't ask me! But since we are doing it, let's go the whole hog. I won't settle for any less. I chose a dark-white miniature schnauzer. On his father's side he goes back right to Frederick the Great; on his mother's side he is related to Excellenz von Stukler. He's as aristocratic as can be. He's even a hemophiliac."

"Excellent," the wife gushed, though I detected a certain tiredness in her voice. "But aren't they going to cheat us?"

"Cheat me? Don't you see how carefully I check everything? From the airport the dog goes straight to the laboratory; then all his documents will undergo a close scrutiny. No one is going to pull a fast one on me. If his tail sticks as much as half an inch upward, I'll send him right back."

"Say, isn't a tail pointing downward a blemish?"

"Not always. There are cases where this is quite the opposite, for instance with Nordic watch dogs."

"I think you are a maniac," the wife opined. "Why can't you make up your mind? After all, it's only a dog."

"Don't rush me, will you? Not in matters of pedigree."

The next three days were very difficult ones. Coughs listened to my excuses behind narrowing eyes. He wouldn't hear of my delaying the dog's homecoming again, though I claimed that I was coordinating it with the upcoming birthday of my little daughter. He asked to see her identity card. Then he grabbed Max and threw her after me over the fence, while shouting obscene remarks about crooks born in the Balkans. I shushed the frightened bitch with a few tender strokes, then hurried to the fence, threw her back into the garden and fled for my life.

"Max has been delayed because of the custom men's strike," I informed the wife. "His history is at present being checked in the genealogical institute in Jerusalem."

"You," the woman fumed, "you and your morbid pedantry!"

But I could see that her resistance had greatly weakened. Max was waiting for me at the street corner, lonely and pathetic. That villain had chased her out of the garden between paroxysms of coughing. I bought the poor little dog a new leather collar with a lot of brass knobs and took her home.

"Straight from Switzerland," I introduced her. "Max."

The whole family looked at her respectfully. This was the first time they had come across a foreign-bred miniature schnauzer who was a real Cohen from the genealogical point of view.

"Beautiful," the wife mumbled. "Really, it has been

worth while waiting for him."

She was already deeply attached to him. And indeed, he is a wonderful bitch, Max is. Her tail is in perpetual movement, like a metronome, and her little eyes shine with wisdom till you have the feeling that she will start speaking any moment. Though personally I hope she won't open her mouth.

❧ The Taming of the Shrew *is a very nice play, but by no flight of the imagination does it apply to our thoroughbred watch bitch, because in the Shakespeare play, if I am not mistaken, the shrew surrenders in the end. In the case of Max it is more appropriate to speak of "The Breaking In of the Tamer."*

Obedience School

Max has in the meantime consolidated her absolute rule in our household. At dawn she jumps on our beds and licks our faces with a frenzy completely defying reason, then without further ado she proceeds to chew up the environment. Our miniature schnauzer has by now eaten up most of our slippers, to say nothing of a number of rugs, a transistor radio and a great deal of literature. About a month ago she also chewed up the northern side of my desk, whereupon I exiled her to the kitchen garden, and since then she does not dare come into the apartment except by day and all through the night.

"Ephraim," the wife asked me, "are we training our dog as we should?"

I also had some doubts on the subject. Our thoroughbred bitch spends most of her leisure on the soft sofas and armchairs of our abode. She receives, tail wagging, every stranger who comes in our door, and starts barking madly only when the little woman tries to play the piano. Besides, the children stuff her with chocolate and mountains of cookies, so that for a schnauzer she looks remarkably hippopotamus-like. She makes puddles on the living-room carpet, to say nothing of worse things. To sum it all up, the dog is a little spoiled.

"Shouldn't we," I asked the wife, "shouldn't we register her in a course?"

I got the idea from looking at Zulu, the black German shepherd dog who lives at the end of our street and passes our house twice a day, clinging to the heels of Dragomir, the dog trainer.

"Heel!" Dragomir shouts from time to time. "Down! Sit!"

And that big, stupid dog obeys him like a machine, sits, jumps as ordered. More than once we watched the humiliating spectacle through our windows.

"He turns that miserable animal into a robot," the woman says pityingly. "Into a soulless robot!"

Our loving glance swept over to our thoroughbred Max, tearing up a lovely embroidered pillow with her sharp teeth, just to see what was inside, and exuding soul all over the place. And last night she again did what is even worse in the middle of the living room.

"Go," the woman therefore mumbled with lowered eyelids. "See Dragomir after all."

Dragomir is a thickset middle-aged man who understands dog language as well as King Solomon did in his heyday, but with humans he is somewhat tongue-tied, because he has been in the country only twenty-six years and is fluent only in Croatian.

"What this?" Dragomir asked when he first met Max. "Where you take this?"

"That does not matter now, sir," I replied, somewhat offended.

Dragomir grabbed Max by the scruff of her neck and lifted her. His eyes bored into the dog's well-cushioned fuselage.

"How you feed dog?"

I told him that Max is fed four times a day soup, roast beef and noodles, or a stew in a special plastic plate we had bought her, but that she does not touch the food, and only an hour or two later when the ants march in from the garden does she walk up to the plate and lick the ants off it. In addition: cream puffs, waffles, Turkish delight.

"Very bad," thus Dragomir. "Dog gets food only once in day and finish. Where dog empties?"

I did not understand. Then I did.

"She always does in the apartment and never in the garden," I complained. "No pleading, no shouting helps. Why?"

"Dog always empties where he did first time because smell," explained the teacher. "How many time he in house?"

I made a quick reckoning. Max is naughty once every two hours, so in three months that adds up to . . .

"About five hundred times."

"*Boje moj!*" Dragomir exclaimed. "Must sell dog."

He explained the situation to us: In a relatively brief time, with perseverance and feeling, we had succeeded in bringing Max to the canine persuasion that the garden was her house and the apartment a toilet.

"Still, what could be done, Maestro?" we asked Dragomir, completely brokenhearted. "Save her. We'll pay you anything!"

"First thing, you tie dog," the trainer laid down the law. "I bring you strong chain."

Max looked at him with deep admiration and wagged her tail like mad. Who said that little dogs are intelligent?

The next day Dragomir showed up with an iron

chain he had removed from a ship, broke a broomstick and stuck it into the ground at the end of the garden, then mercilessly tied thoroughbred Max to it.

"So," he said. "Stays like that all the time. Once a day eats a little. Nobody goes to her."

Our hearts skipped a beat.

"But she will cry," I protested weakly. "She is accustomed to company. She will cry."

"Cry, cry," roared Dragomir. "No kutchimuchi."

He was rather frightening, Dragomir was, but he had unusual authority. Personally I did not like him because he had yellow teeth.

"But," I mumbled, "this is only an interim arrangement, isn't it?"

"Why interior?"

Dragomir again suggested that we should sell the dog. This was not a miniature schnauzer, he claimed. This was simply a runt; it was a pity to waste good money on it. I solemnly promised him that we would strictly adhere to his instructions. We would do anything if only he would not take the dog away.

Dragomir mellowed somewhat. "O.K. So, hundred fifty without receipt now here."

Max started to whimper. At long last she smelled a rat.

By afternoon the whole household was in tears. The children watched Max pining away in the diaspora of the garden, throwing heart-rending glances at them. Max looked so miserable, so lonely, so sad. My daughter Ranana broke into bitter sobs, burst outdoors and lay down next to Max in a spontaneous demonstration of international solidarity. Her brother Amir kept pestering me that we should free the dog for a little while at least, but I stood as firm as the Rock of Gibraltar.

"Sorry," I said. "An obedience course is an obedience course."

"For fifteen minutes," the woman implored me. "Five minutes."

In the end I weakened. O.K., five minutes on the dot. Max Liberata tore into the house like a snowstorm and licked us uninhibitedly. She spent the night in the nursery, curled up in Amir's featherbed, and ate cakes and shoes.

Dragomir rang in the morning. "How dog night?"

"All right," I answered. "Everything's fine, as it should be."

"Bark?"

"Let her bark!"

Max was sitting on my chest taking an interest in my glasses.

Dragomir explained to me over the telephone that in the first stage it was very important to maintain an iron discipline.

"Rest assured, old boy," I answered into the receiver. "Once I spend a fortune on the dog's education, I want to see results!"

Dragomir calmed down. I disentangled the telephone cord from Max's teeth and turned to everyday matters, greatly relieved.

At lunchtime Amir broke through the door in a panic. "Quick!" the vigilant child shouted. "Dragomir!"

We took Max off the piano in a jiffy, ran with her to the other end of the garden and tied her to the stick with the ship's chain. By the time the trainer arrived we were all sitting around the table eating like a well-ordered family.

"Where dog?" the trainer asked.

"Where should it be?" said the wife. "In its place,

in the garden."

"Very good," he said. "No release."

We mutely motioned that that was obvious. And indeed Max stayed tied up till the end of our lunch. After we ate our fruit, Amir dashed out and returned her to the bosom of the family. Max was happy, though a little confused. She found it rather difficult to understand during the coming weeks why she was always being grabbed and tied to the stake whenever that gentleman who spoke so much nonsense came and why she was taken back to the toilet once he had left. But altogether it went off quite nicely.

Naturally, we had to watch out very carefully for the coming of the trainer, but that was what we had a watch dog for, wasn't it? From time to time we would give Dragomir detailed reports on the day's extraordinary progress, ask him for advice on building a kennel out in the garden (no need, not cold outside) on how to clean the chain and other important matters. On that Tuesday when Max pulled the cloth off the table and chewed it up we even raised Dragomir's salary for the sake of credibility.

That weekend Dragomir made the mistake of his life. He showed up in the evening.

Naturally, it was Zulu who was to blame. That black dog had bitten the postman in the neck, and Dragomir had been alerted at nightfall to have a man-to-man talk with the dog. And since he was in the neighborhood, he dropped in, through the open kitchen door, and advanced unchecked to the nursery. There he found Max in close embrace with Amir in his bed, the two of them watching television and eating pretzels.

"This garden?" Dragomir roared, his face beet-red. "Where he tied, this?"

"Sorry." Amir pulled the blanket over his head. "We didn't know you were coming."

I fled straight to the bathroom and took a cold shower, underscored by hysterical shrieks, but the wife suddenly erupted with unusual firmness.

"Nothing garden, nothing tying up!" the little one shrilled straight into the face of the Balkan monster. "This is not a prisoner, sir, this is a dog! What you take this for, a concentration camp?"

"Crazy woman," Dragomir dryly commented. "She will always do it inside."

"Let her! I clean up after her, not you!"

And she kicked that amateur down the stairs. Since then Max again infiltrates our sofas legally, and the wife runs after her with a ready rag. And the dog again eats four or five times a day, is very free and also very fat, and we talk to her three time in day, and no garden and finish.

❦ After such rich experiences in the animal world, we thought it only right to write a long essay on a zoological subject. Then we found that it was not so easy to locate an unclaimed beast for literary purposes.

Animal Farm

"Listen, old boy," our publisher said to us the other night. "Before you start writing a new book I'd like you to realize that no one reads any longer in this country."

"Don't exaggerate," I answered obstinately. "They say that in Haifa there lives a couple who buy a few books every year."

"Maybe," the publisher said. "I heard about them myself. But you can't build a whole edition on this couple. So I suggest that you, too, start writing for the kids. They force them at school to buy books."

"O.K.," I said to our publisher. "I'll write a children's book. What's selling now?"

"Animals."

"All right, so I'll write about some animal."

"Which?"

"I haven't yet thought it over. Let's say I'll write about a kid: *Kiddie, Son of Billy Goat.*"

"Don't kid yourself," the publisher retorted. "That's old-hat: *Adventures of Kiddie the Kid*. We sold eight printings. Quite a nice story. Kiddie the Kid escapes from home and travels to town in a jeep but after many adventures realizes that home is still best and returns to Nanny goat, his mother. You'll have to find a rarer animal, my boy, because children's books have been written about almost all of them."

"How about a bear?"

"Last week I published the last of the series *Tommy the Polar Bear*. Tommy escapes from home and climbs up a flagpole, but in the end he returns home because he realizes that home is best after all. We have had it all before, my dear sir—cats, cows, butterflies, deer, zebras, antelopes . . ."

"How about the hyena?"

"Too late. *Heinous the Hyena Joins the Underground*. Sixteen printings."

"He flees from home . . ."

"Yes. In a jeep. You have to find something new."

"Anteater?"

"Oh, that's a best seller now. *Anton the Anteater in Tel Aviv*. He flees home . . ."

"Bat?"

"*Betty the Bat and Her Forty Suitors*. Adventures of a little bat who stupidly leaves her parents . . ."

"But she returns?"

"Of course. In a jeep."

Our publisher rose and went down to the storeroom.

"It's hard to find a free animal," he mumbled while searching feverishly on the shelves. "Look, *Felix the Falcon at the Olympic Games, Coco the Jolly Snail* and *The Story of Armand the Armadillo* who runs away from home to become an armorer . . ."

"I've got it," I shouted. "Rainworm! . . ."

"Twenty-three printings," our publisher scoffed. "*Rainier the Rainworm Goes to Sea*. Quite exciting adventures. He goes aboard a schooner . . ."

"How?"

"He hides among a shipment of jeeps."

"I see. So I guess all that's left is the bedbug."

"*Bugsy the Bug Cheats the Customs.* Came out this fall. She flees her parents' home through the back door. Not bad at all . . ."

"How about snakes?"

"Splendid. *Vicky the Friendly Viper at the Three-Ring Circus.* She makes friends with the neighbor's little boy and they run away together with Mitzi the Mosquito."

"Carps?"

"*Karl the Carp in the Air Force.*"

"Oysters?"

"*Oyez the Oyster in Court.* He and his twin brother crawl out of their shell, but after a while they return home because of the cold."

"All right," I sighed, "a sea sponge."

"Excellent!" Our publisher's face lighted up. "I think that's not been done yet. But you have to hurry because if they discover it there'll be three editions out within the week."

"Leave it to me," I assured him. "You can start printing the dust jacket: *Spooky the Sponge Goes to Town.*"

"Get cracking!"

I ran home, panting. This morning I finished the first volume of the series. The plot is quite ingenious: Spooky flees his parents' home to become a kitchen sponge in Jerusalem, but after all kinds of misadventures he returns home. I think I'll have him ride a jeep. One has to play it safe.

When a writer comes up with what he calls a "true-life story," he means to say that his is such a brilliant talent that in his work fantasy and reality become indistinguishable. Well, the story below is honest-to-God true, though it will be appreciated only by professional parents, students and babies. It deals with a Hebrew babysitter, or, to be more specific, with our last sitter but one.

Josepha the Free

Ever since we moved into the southern end of town we have become partisans of academic babysitting. From time to time we pick out a pretty student from the nearby campus, philosophy and archaeology by preference, and give her the run of our brood. The kids take to them easily and everything looks dandy till, one day, the big machine starts to creak and our sitter isn't free in the evenings any more, and she's got exams, or she's only got Wednesday, and even then she's cramming together with Gideon, and we come home on Wednesday and they're both on the couch with ears pink from studying, and the cushions are crumpled and Gideon is combing his hair. And the wife says to me, "That little hussy's already found herself someone."

And that, as a rule, puts a stop to the meteoric career of a babysitter, and the next student enters the picture.

This time it was Josepha.

She aroused great hopes at her first, self-effacing appearance: so small, so fragile, so bespectacled. The little woman took her for a girl of thirteen, but it turned out she had already passed twenty on her spindly legs. Josepha invariably wore slacks, and instead of speaking she rustled, a few words at a time and with lowered eyes. Numerous moles studded her white face and she was altogether a little mole herself. In brief: an ideal, long-play babysitter.

And indeed Josepha bore out our shrewd evaluation to the full. She would show up on the dot, rustle a *shalom* and settle down in the kids' room to copy out something into umpteen notebooks.

She never read, she never wrote; she just copied all the time, and that got on our nerves, but we swallowed it because after all no one is perfect except Golda. Besides, Josepha differed from all the rest of our academic babysitters in one striking quality: She was always free. Any time we would ring her up on the phone she would whisper unhesitatingly, "I'm free."

"Could you come a bit earlier?"

"Yes."

"And stay later?"

"Yes."

And before long she would come to copy, silently and with lowered eyes. At night I used to take her home in an absolute hush. Only once I cracked and asked her what they were teaching these days at her faculty, and Josepha said into the darkness, "Thank you."

And that put an end to our lively conversation. But otherwise she was a model sitter: soundproof, never engaged, always Josepha. We were very happy with her, and the kids too respected her monastic silence despite her thinness. Now and then we would invite her to join us for supper, but she always refused, in deadly fear of something. My wife was of the opinion that she never ate.

"The poor kid," mused the wife one barren night. "It just isn't natural that a young girl like that should always be free."

The symptom was really worrying. Morning and evening and a quarter past three in the afternoon— Josepha is always ready to copy-sit. Once we rang her up at 11:45 P.M., when all the crickets had already fallen asleep outside.

"Are you free?"

"Yes."

"Can you come right away?"

"Yes."

The wife replaced the receiver with moist eyes. "It's tragic," she muttered. "She hasn't got a soul. No one in the whole wide world . . ."

This period of heartfelt commiseration and pangs of social conscience lasted a full month. Then I found my wife getting a bit mad at her.

"Must say I find it peculiar," grumbled the wife. "She's got an emotional block somewhere, that girl has."

The problem began to preoccupy my wife and she showed signs of deep psychological upset. Sometimes, following a call to sit, she would pound the wall with her fist:

"She's free again! Free!"

That Saturday the little woman slipped out of bed at 2:30 A.M. and sleepwalked to the phone.

"Josepha, are you free?"

"Yes."

"Now?"

"Yes."

"Thanks, no need."

By then she nursed a fierce hatred for her. She had concluded that Josepha must be mad. Something hereditary, no doubt, something from her infancy. A vision of Josepha at twelve appeared before our eyes, sitting in class and looking like seven most likely.

"Here are my favorite pupils," says the teacher. "Tirza the brainy, Ziva the naughty and Josepha the free."

What shall I tell you? Last Independence Day she was free. Yes indeed, on Independence Day! All that day she baby-sat and copied all night till dawn. The little one nearly wept.

"That a girl her age shouldn't have at least one wretched boyfriend," the kind woman sobbed. "What's she going about in pants for on those two matchsticks all the time? Why doesn't she get rid of those moles? What does she think she is?"

The wife claimed that Josepha's eyes were perfect and that she wore spectacles only to put off potential suitors. I was afraid that if the problem wasn't solved my wife would soon lose her emotional balance. I consulted a doctor and as a result of his advice asked the neighbors' grown sons to drop in of an evening under the flimsiest of excuses.

Josepha sat at the table and copied, totally paralyzed. She would offer the boys her damp and flustered hand like a broken wing and say without looking up, "Josepha."

The wife just went to pieces. "That's no Josepha," she groaned. "That's a Joseph."

The turning point came in the shape of Naftali, little-Ronit-on-our-left's big brother. This hefty, hairy-legged fellow wasn't put off by our frozen babysitter like the other candidates, but sat down by her side and followed the copying with deep interest, speechless as yet but still . . . In the end they shook hands again, as my wife informed me from her observation point, and passions began to flare.

"Maybe," whispered the woman, "maybe now."

That Tuesday it happened. The wife rang Josepha to ask if she'd be free tonight, and the line hummed with the sensational reply: "No."

"What? No?" said the woman.

"I'm busy."

It was a triumph of sheer will power over an unparalleled social depression.

We stayed home basking in the joy of creation and said hosannas.

Josepha has found herself someone at last, is not maddeningly free any more, is on the way to complete recovery, thank God. It gives me pleasure to inform the public at large that from that Tuesday things began to move at a pace.

"Sorry," Josepha said into the mouthpiece. "I'm engaged."

"Engaged," she had said like a big girl. Delightful.

"And tomorrow?"

"Only till nine."

That is to say, a normalization of international relations. We were as proud as peacocks. We'd got the poor girl back on the track after all, had saved a Jewish maiden, hadn't we? So we sat in our spacious home, very satisfied, except that it bothered us a little that we were sitting at home, as I said, unable to go out because of Josepha. Outrageous, in fact. After all, one might have expected some loyalty from a frivolous slip of a girl whom a man has, so to say, lifted out of the gutter with his own two hands.

When the rumor reached us that Josepha and Naftali were seen walking together by moonlight while we ourselves were confined to barracks, the woman's dam burst: "The little hussy!" she wailed. "The first boy who whistles and she goes crawling on all fours."

We'd have traded in the little sex maniac for another copyist without a quiver but for the attachment of the kids, who had meanwhile grown used to the world of silence. So we just swallowed the recurring insult of her "Sorry, I'm not free."

The cup of bitterness overflowed on the dark night of July 21. We were coming home from the movies and noticed a young couple under the lamplight. Him and her, who else? Walking at their leisure in the middle of the night in pregnant silence.

"Good night," Josepha said as they passed us, whereupon the little one could contain herself no longer.

"I thought, my dear," she spat at the little hussy, "that you were preparing for exams!"

Naftali leaped to her defense. "She studies all the time. She's been babysitting for us and I'm just taking her home now."

Josepha's eyes plunged to hitherto unknown depths, and her fragile figure with the fake moles vanished through the mist. The woman mumbled ancient oaths and I swore, there and then in the middle of the road, that henceforth I'd take on nothing but dishes, nothing but smashing blond dishes, dammit.

❧ *The time has now come to go on a little trip and do a spot of folkloristic research. Take, for instance, Austria, the blue-and-white, quarter-karat diamond in Central Europe. It has two outstanding features: the severe cold which sweeps down from the mountains and the pleasant old ladies of Vienna who sweep down on us from the wings. The two taken together are a deadly combination.*

The Coathangers
of Vienna

Winter is a serious affair in Vienna. Whoever goes outdoors without an overcoat on his back runs an excellent chance of subsisting on aspirin for the next few days. However, as soon as you enter any place of public entertainment, a silver-haired Austrian grandmother shoots up out of the ground and says, "*Garderobe.*"

Which is "cloakroom" in Deutsch. With that, she takes your overcoat and drags it to her lair, never to be seen again except on your way out, against a ransom. As a matter of fact, she doesn't ask for money; she only returns the kidnapped coat and says, "*Danke schoen.*"

Once, in a big Vienna theater, I asked the local crone, "How much do I owe you?"

She answered, "The usual."

That is, she isn't interested in the remuneration; she doesn't do this for the money but for the excitement. She is a fixture of the Austrian capital; she is one of Vienna's famous coat removers. Their single-minded devotion to the cause is proverbial. A fly cannot get into one of the city's restaurants without removing its coat. Once, if memory serves me, I intended only to say a word to an acquaintance in the renowned Sacher patisserie. I dashed past the hag on duty, but before I had reached the end of the hall the remover barred my way.

"*Garderobe.*"

"Just a moment, ma'am," I threw at her and continued on my way in. "Only a word, *bitte.*"

She blocked my further progress. I jumped aside to bypass her, but she dived and caught my coat. I shook her off and skillfully dribbled past her. The old lady caught me in a running tackle and held onto my knees with her two hands. It was a brief but bitter struggle. You wouldn't believe what powerful, sinewy arms these old women have. She impounded my coat, with a few deft dabs cleaned me of all traces of the fight, and hung the coat carefully on a hanger. Then she stuck a number on the coat and handed me a counterfoil bearing the same number. I pushed the slip in my pocket, went into Sacher's, shouted "Eight o'clock!" at Friedrich, turned on my heel, took out the slip and gave it to the old lady. Thereupon she took the coat off its hanger, removed a few strands of invisible lint from it, as well as the number, and said, "*Danke schoen.*"

I gave her ten shillings, a fortune even by international standards, meaning to bribe her so that she wouldn't stop me next time, but she accepted the gift with equanimity. As I said, for the Vienna removers, money is only a means, not an end. One has only to look into their tired eyes framed by a sallow and covetous face to realize that they live for their daily coats. Take away your coat from them and you have taken away their *raison d'être.* It's a sort of addiction, like hashish.

It once happened that a group of irate citizens organized themselves and burst into a hotel all at the same time, dispersing like lightning with their coats into the far corners of the building. In such emergencies the old monster divides herself into three or four submonsters and shows up in every corner, in a genuine witch hunt, and collects the contraband coats one by one, saying, "*Garderobe.*"

I saw with my own eyes how a respected aged Austrian poet swallowed hard and refused to surrender his coat. He buttoned it right up and clutched it to his shriveled body with a strength belying his years, like the clerk in Gogol's "The Coat."

"I won't," he bawled and pressed his bloodless lips together. "I'm sick. I'm running a temperature. I don't want to."

The overripe hat-check girl stood behind him mutely for a whole hour, never for a second removing her eyes from the object of her lust. In the end the distinguished poet broke down and handed over his coat peacefully. One could smell violence in the air.

"Why?" I asked my hotel manager. "Why do they remove everyone's coat?"

"Don't know," the man answered, his eyes shifting nervously. "It's forbidden to bring in coats."

"But why?"

"They might get crumpled."

They are everywhere, the grandmas of Vienna. To the end of my days I shall remember the time I was sitting in a posh cinema when suddenly I felt a light tug from below. The old lady had crawled under the chairs up to my coat and now breathed into the darkness, "*Garderobe.*"

What is the solution? It is said that a Latin American tourist who had gone off his rocker in Vienna because of the perpetual coat badgering one day wrapped his naked body in a fur coat and when the old lady at his hotel unwrapped him he was left in the altogether in the middle of the crowded lobby. The old lady handed him his number without batting an eyelid and placidly hung up the coat. They are as fanatical as the Chinese; they have a solid ideological grounding. One night, for instance, in a fiat of uncharacteristic recklessness, I burst past the old crone of a central hotel and succeeded in jumping into an elevator and soaring up to the sixteenth floor.

"*Garderobe*," the old lady whispered, standing ramrod straight in front of the elevator door on the sixteenth floor. Personally, I was badly winded, while she was only blinking. She folded my coat carefully on her brawny arms and ran down into her hutch.

They are a remarkable breed.

The day before my departure from the capital of the Hapsburgs I was awakened at midnight by a sudden crash. The door of my hotel room was smashed in and fell off its hinges. The old woman burst in and made straight for the closet. She took my coat out together with its hanger.

"Sir," she hissed, "kiss it goodbye."

Naturally it was only a silly dream. In the morning my coat was returned undamaged at the downstairs cloakroom. The number 107 was still sticking to it.

For the first time in centuries, the peaceful Swiss had some firsthand experience of civil war. It started as usual with the seizing of a radio station and ended with the bodily removal of the author from the Canton of Zurich.

How I Pulled a William Tell on the Swiss

At the end of the broadcast the interviewer of Radio Zurich asked me whether I did not find a certain similarity between his country and ours. I replied that there definitely was some similarity. Our respective neighbors particularly resembled each other, and with that the lively conversation came to an end and all that was left was to wind up the interview in a dignified way.

"It is customary on this program," the interviewer announced, "to ask our guest to choose a record of his liking, which we then broadcast to our listeners. So please . . ."

This came as a complete surprise. And besides, I'm not particularly fond of records; my family is all I care about. My instinct for self-preservation whispered in my ear to choose "Havah Nagilah," which is quite foolproof, but I dropped the idea right away, assuming that the Swiss, too, are allergic to the song. I decided therefore to pay a nice compliment to the host country and proposed to the interviewer in a clear and ringing voice, "I'm simply nuts about the famous Swiss yodel-ing."

The interviewer looked at me somewhat surprised, then shrugged and motioned me out. As I left the studio I heard through the loudspeakers the Alpine singer riding the roller coaster—*holalio!* To tell the absolute truth, I was never too hot on yodeling; it always reminds me of my bar-mitzvah age when my voice changed and I almost died of shame.

But why not be nice to them?

On returning to my hotel I found a local man wearing a National Guard cap waiting for me. He briefly asked my name, then inquired, "What have we done to you, sir?"

"I beg your pardon?"

"You should not have insulted us so vilely," the inhabitant continued, his face reddening. "My wife told me, go and tell that gentleman that the Swiss nation will never forgive him this stinging insult!"

And with that he turned on his heel and left, his eyes burning with restrained anger. I went up to my room in a pensive mood. The elderly elevator boy asked me between the third and fourth floors, "You the guy who ordered the yodel?"

"Yes," I answered. "Why?"

The oldster did not reply, only his earlobes twitched. From my room I rang one of my friends in Zurich. "Listen," I related to Oscar, "they asked me at the radio station what was my favorite music and I said the yodel."

There was an ominous silence at the other end. It lasted for a minute or two, maybe more.

"Stay in the hotel," my pal finally said. "I'll be with you in a few minutes."

In the meantime I had another call. Someone asked whether it was me, and after I identified myself he spat into the receiver. Oscar arrived deathly pale and locked the door behind him.

"I didn't tell my wife," he whispered. "How did this happen, for goodness' sake?"

"Dunno," I answered. "A moment of weakness. Why? What's the matter?"

"Look, pal," Oscar said, "you have hurt their deepest feelings."

From his halting words I understood that the Swiss nation was blessed with the best nature could offer its creatures. It has excellent banks, watches and chocolates, but there is a severe blemish on its history: the nightmare of the national yodel which follows them wherever they go, though they themselves shun it as if it were the proverbial plague. According to the Swiss, this is a sort of infantile music which hurts their image as a self-respecting nation. They have a point there. After all, man's voice is not a yo-yo skipping up and down, up and down without ever stopping.

"Haven't they kicked you out of the hotel?" Oscar asked.

"Not yet."

"We have a big basement," Oscar mused. "In a few weeks the storm will have blown over, I hope."

With that he hurried off. I went to the window and looked out. A number of men were crowding around the hotel entrance looking upward. I hid behind the curtain. Should they attack, I'll fire back. They won't get me without a fight.

I rang up the broadcasting studio and asked for my interviewer. The switchboard was still operating.

"The building is surrounded," I informed the interviewer. "Why didn't you warn me at the end of the broadcast?"

"This is a democratic country," the man answered icily. "If someone feels he has to slap our face, let him. You could have chosen marvelous songs, such as 'Havah Nagilah,' but no, you must insult us, sir."

"Hello!"

But he had already slammed down the receiver. I went to the window and peeped out cautiously from behind the curtain. The crowd below had been swelled by a number of cops, soldiers on leave and senior government officials. Maybe they had by now taken up positions all over the hotel and were waiting for hunger to speed me down the stairs. I rang room service and ordered two days' iron rations. It took about an hour before they knocked at my door. I dismantled the barricade I had set up with cupboards, armchairs and a heavy sofa.

The hotel manager himself stood in the doorway, a tray in his hands.

"The waiters refuse to serve you, sir," he informed me coolly, and added, "Why did you do it?"

"Simple," I answered. "I like yodeling, yooolala-heeo!"

In all sincerity I must confess I had no intention whatsoever of yodeling. It burst from my throat quite involuntarily. I was surprised at the pristine pureness of my voice, though it had a certain recitative tinge. The manager's eyes opened wide in amazement, then he fled my room snorting in anger. I did not dare to touch the food he had brought lest it be poisoned. Instead I decided to hunt pigeons on the roof and fry them on a slow fire. With food and water assured, I mused, I could stand a long siege. Eventually we would find a way out; the Embassy would intervene, or I could have plastic surgery and then I could thumb my nose at them.

Toward evening I opened the window a crack but jumped back right away, fearing rocks would start flying. It seems that never since William Tell and his apple had anyone united the Swiss people to such an extent. The first cables started coming in: "THE ARABS ARE RIGHT. YOU ARE INGRATE BASTARDS," or simply "PIG, G. FLEISHHACKER." I rejected two challenges to duel. The telephone never stopped ringing.

"As of today I speak no Yiddish," a lawyer notified me from nearby Basel. "I'm through!"

"What were you trying to achieve with your perverse irony?" someone whined. "What, for goodness' sake, what?"

"My aim," I answered, "is to restore to the traditional yodel the respect the nation owes it. Yoolala-heeio!"

This again was quite spontaneous. The yoolalaheeio had burst from my throat like a gushing spring and my Adam's apple jumped up and down like a well-oiled piston. A slight dizziness gripped me, a sort of spiritual deliverance I had never before experienced. I suppose the ancient condemned must have felt such an elation as they stretched out their necks to the executioner, yodeling gaily.

I threw the window wide open. Down in the street a mob, lit by the torches they were carrying, was clamoring for my head. Here and there I spotted a portrait of the late President Nasser carried aloft; a few hummed the Swiss national anthem.

I opened my arms wide and for a second a deep hush fell on the square.

"Yollah-yollah-yoholliloh!" the song burst forth from my throat. "Yollla-yehollo-yeholliloh."

The police dispersed the mob with their night sticks and put out the fire. That very night they smuggled me out of Switzerland in a sealed railway car, disguised as Lenin.

The other day Oscar wrote me—anonymously, it goes without saying—that things were calming down gradually. Some liberal voices were being raised in favor of renewing my entry permit to the Canton of Zurich, but to my great regret I can never again travel there because should I as much as even think of Switzerland, I immediately burst out yodeling at the top of my voice. This is an irresistible urge—yoholaheeho. Oh dear, here I go again.

❦ *To the best of our knowledge, no one ever asked for the minority opinion at the bullfight—that is, nobody is interested in hearing how the bull feels about it all. It seems that this is a first attempt in this field and, of all people, it had to be undertaken by a Hebrew writer. Or could it be that this is no mere coincidence?*

Bullshit Artists

The *corrida* is a national institution in Spain, just like the eating of steaks in Texas. The two are even related, but the Spaniards like their steak on the hoof. The charging bull therefore becomes a daily commodity and even the unofficial arms of the state. Small wonder then that we had hardly landed in beautiful Barcelona when we excitedly asked the first customs officer we ran into, "Is any *corrida* still due to take place?" "*Sí*," the man answered, "the last one this year. You lucky bastard!" It appears that with the arrival of the rains, Spanish bulls heave a sigh of relief, and we had arrived just before the gates of the arena were to be locked up for the winter.

"You don't know how lucky you are, Señor," the sons of Catalonia said to me, their eyes flashing. "Miguel is in town!"

This sounded most encouraging: Miguel. My old acquaintance, a respected Barcelona lawyer, bought us a couple of very good seats, exactly beneath the ornate box of the honorary President, who would signal Miguel with a special handkerchief when to slaughter the bull. At least 60,000 sports- and meat-loving aficionados were crowding the monster stadium. Half of them were American tourists and one a perplexed Israeli. The atmosphere was extremely tense. Everyone realized that the clash between the bull and Miguel was inevitable. Raven-haired, demure señoritas were waving their fans, and in their beautiful eyes one could read genocide. We went on chewing gum placidly, but our emotions were in a turmoil.

"Look," our lawyer called. "Miguel!"

Into the arena stepped a brigade of cavalry equipped with light arms, followed by the matador's personal aides, and finally Miguel himself, who was very lean and resplendent in embroidered silks. He bowed deeply to us and we gave him the thumbs-down greeting. In the meantime my lawyer checked the program, stopping at the list of bulls which featured names, weight and marital status.

"My God!" he whispered. "These are very dangerous bulls!"

I asked him whether he hated bulls. My lawyer reflected for a while, then assured me that he did not hate them, though he despised them for their morbid aggressiveness toward toreadors. I inquired of him what would be the fate of a pacifist bull who refused to fight. It seems that such conscientious objectors are deprived of all civil rights. A good-looking cow is ushered in and she promptly draws the shlemiel out of the arena. Such a miserable bull as this has to wait months, figuratively pawing the ground with impatience, before he gets another chance to be butchered.

Luckily our bull was carved from sterner material. He stormed into the arena and immediately charged the red cloth waved by the picadors or whatever you call them. These did not lose their cool but scattered in all directions and jumped the fence in mortal fear. A storm of protest arose all around us. Men jumped to their feet and shook their fists at the bloodthirsty beast, while the women threw kisses to the innocently persecuted picadors.

"What the hell are you running about there for?" my lawyer yelled at the bull. "Who do you think you are, you sonofabitch?"

The bull stopped in his tracks and squinted up at us.

"What are you staring at there?" the lawyer roared. "Charge, damn it!"

The bull lowered his horns and rushed a beribboned attendant.

"Stop him!" my lawyer shouted. "This bull is a murderer!"

And indeed it was quite an ugly sight that a bull should be so hostile toward mankind, just because he's being stabbed from all sides, and spears, hooks and national flags are being stuck into his flesh. Look, now his horns have almost touched one of the sportsmen, who has done him no harm except wave a red cloth in his face. The audience is seething with hatred; the lynch atmosphere grows ever stronger. Reinforcements thirty strong flow into the arena, armed with pikes, armor and automatic weapons. The management's first helicopters appear over the arena carrying air-to-surface missiles. The bull stops, hugging the wall and breathing heavily.

"You coward," my lawyer shouts. "Is that how they taught you to fight?"

The bull raises his eyes to him. "I want to fight?"

"Yes, you," the lawyer replies and turns to the butchers. "Kill him, boys, kill him quickly; otherwise by the Madonna of Seville I'll come down there myself!"

In the end self-discipline gained the upper hand,

and he did not go down. The women started throwing kisses at the armored knight who had entered the arena to the fanfare of massed bugles.

"Is that Miguel?" I asked.

"No. The bull is not yet tired enough," my seat neighbors explained and poured their scorn on the goings-on below. "Come on, buster, you miserable cow, let's see what you can do now!"

Several more took to jeering, "Cow!" The bull lunged at the horse and toppled it on its rider.

"Police!" the bleachers echoed. "This is not a bull. This is a public menace!"

"Attack innocent horses, will you?" My lawyer jumped to his feet. "This is where you die, you creep!"

It was evident that the bull could not stand lawyers. Actually, by now he could hardly stand on his feet at all and was clearly suffering from a bad case of persecution mania. Personally, I decided to look at matters from his point of view and found that it was a sadly depressing situation: foreign soil, a hostile audience, overwhelming numerical superiority. But it was too late in the day for philosophical meditation. The women threw kisses with increased energy. Miguel returned to the arena with orchestral accompaniment, in his hands an outsized sword. He was wearing an elegant cape and exuded health and vigor. At first he went through a number of classic exercises with the red cloth he was carrying, while the audience sighed with pleasure. Every time the bull punctured the air with his horns, Miguel shouted, "*Olé!*"

He also kept taunting the bull.

"Where are you, bully-boy? Now show us what you can do! Oops, baby, oops! You just try to touch me and I'll make mincemeat of you, so help me, *olé!*"

The women showered him with flowers. Miguel drew his sword and prepared for the dignified ritual slaughter.

"The sword must pierce the lungs, kidneys, heart and intestines," my lawyer exclaimed, "with a single stroke delivered with great virtuosity."

Miguel rose on his toes like a ballet dancer and stuck the blade into the trembling beast's back. But he must have pierced only two or three of his targets, because the bull did not drop to his knees. Quite to the contrary, he seemed to have recovered somewhat. The mob's raving hatred overflowed all bounds.

"Hey, what's the matter?" they roared at the bull. "Drop dead immediately!"

My lawyer rolled his program into a bullhorn. "Malingerer!" he shouted. "Behave like a man, you rotten chicken!"

The bull was properly fed up. He stepped up to the President's box. "Sir," he shouted, "if you don't take this louse off my back I won't play bull!"

The President waved him away. "I don't talk to bulls! Kill him!"

Miguel rose to his full height, raised his sword, and in a flash a whole division of reinforcements burst in to madden the enemy for him. I realize it is difficult to overcome the bloodthirsty beast as long as he can stand on his own four legs. So they threw at him another twenty darts, poisoned arrows and tear gas.

"This is the end," the lawyer predicted. "Now he'll get his comeuppance!"

It turns out that if the torero kills his bull skillfully enough the President makes him a gift of the bull's ear. Should he do his job with a brilliance beyond the call of duty and should the slaughter be absolutely outstanding, he gets the tail as well. The toreros are Spain's most admired millionaires. Men are happy to touch the fringes of their jackets, women send them love letters and toreros learn to read them at night school. They are true acrobats, these brave Miguels, as they stand erect, stalking the raging monster who is at the end of his tether.

"Now you'll see something," my lawyer predicted. "Miguel will drop to his knees and execute a brilliant veronica. That is, at the very last moment he will move aside with devilish skill and thrust his sword into the heart of this maddened beast."

The band played a gay march, then came an ominous roll of drums. Miguel dropped to his knees and the bull charged him according to plan. At the last moment Miguel moved aside. So did the bull. Miguel sailed through the air and landed spread-eagled on the hot sand.

The spectators' patience had run out.

"Enough," they shouted at the bull. "What brutality, you sadist!"

Some spectators were calling for a doctor. The bull rolled Miguel in front of him with much feeling, then he lifted him on his horns and tossed the torero high above his head.

I jumped to my feet:

"*Olé!*" I shouted at the top of my lungs.

My lawyer darted a murderous glance at me, but by then nothing could stop me.

"Bravo!" I roared. "Let him have it! Don't spare the creep!"

I blew kisses at the brave bull, and when the legendary Miguel arced through the air for the third time, I tore up my program and scattered it ecstatically. Then

I threw my necktie, my shirt and a shoe at the victor. According to some witnesses I even sang the march from *Carmen* in a falsetto voice. But at this stage more reinforcements tore into the arena, headed by two armored cars and fresh toreadors with drawn swords. I could stand it no longer, took leave of my downcast lawyer and fled. As I passed under the colonnade on my way out I heard the victory roars of the crowd and I understood that at long last they had succeeded in knocking off the bull with a concentrated barrage of mortar bombs. The toreador probably got a tail and a half, while three tired nags towed his victim outside. On the other hand, I also saw the great Miguel placed in an ambulance, and that made me feel better. I grabbed the first taxi and made straight for Tel Aviv, to my little sons who will never become toreadors because of their red hair. I'll just have to reconcile myself to that, once and for all.

The ancient struggle between the Jews and the authorities in this part of the world for the right to travel abroad has been waged ever since the first Zionist Congress in Basel. At that time the Turks delayed the delegates' departure with clever administrative chicaneries, while nowadays the Israeli government works with a gigantic travel tax designed to turn every traveler into a flying bankrupt. The proverbially ingenious Jews defend themselves in an original way: with theatrical hits. At first this sounds somewhat strange, but as the Bard ought to have said, "There's no business like show business."

The Fight over Rights

The other day Felix Selig accosted me on the stairs between the first and second floors.

"Excuse me," my neighbor said, "are you going to America again?"

"No," I answered. "Why?"

"It doesn't matter, really," said Felix. "I only wanted to ask you to buy me the musical *Hello, Dolly!* but never mind. I'll write my brother-in-law."

Before long I understood: Felix had heard that the old lady who runs the corner pharmacy had been to London last summer and had bought herself the rights to three Agatha Christie thrillers. Now she had sold them to one of the theaters for a handsome profit. And that had prompted Felix to act. According to his information, most Israeli tourists abroad are looking for plays in view of the huge demand on the local market sparked by the country's theatrical boom. Rights are the "in" thing now. Especially musicals. For a smash hit the producers and the theaters are ready to lay down real money.

"The owner of the laundry downstairs has three Dürenmatts," Felix disclosed. "The Chamber Theater and the Haifa Municipal Theater are bidding for the rights, but he won't sell now because he's afraid there might be another devaluation."

You can't be too careful nowadays. Take, for instance, Habima. They approached the famous French playwright Anouilh for the rights to the historical drama *Becket* and found that only two days before they had been snapped up by a carpenter from Netanya who had been visiting his sister in Paris. Now the carpenter is willing to give up the Hebrew rights on condition Habima lets him build the sets. Negotiations are dragging on because the workers' committee of the theater opposes the hiring of outside carpenters. It is said that the Workers' Federation owns an Ionesco.

"Very interesting," I remarked. "And isn't it difficult to buy rights?"

"Nothing to it," said Felix. "You only have to say that you are an impresario, actor or usher in Israel and plunk down a few dollars on the table. It's a safe investment. The National Theater the other week bought two Tennessee Williamses on the black market.

"It was quite a complicated deal. The rights had been purchased in New York by an El-Al steward, who had introduced himself to the playwright's agent as Israel's Minister of Education and Culture. Then he sold the rights to a veteran actress here, who intended in this way to assure for herself the leading-lady's part. As the management of the theater did not agree to this, she

exchanged the two Tennessees for a Max Frish drama,
which until then had been held by a basketball player
who had bought them in a Greek pawnshop. As soon
as the Chamber Theater learned of the transaction,
they contacted the basketball player and snatched the
two Tennessees from under the nose of Habima."

"Just a second," I interrupted Felix hoarsely. "If
Max Frish is still available, I'm buying!"

Selig promised to check. We'll see. As this article
went to press Frish had gone up by two points. Brecht
is firm. There is excess demand for Millers. Linked musicals are distributing 6 percent dividends.

❧ *Only a few years ago violence became fashionable as an omnibus solution to the individual's problems in society, and since then it has taken the free world by storm. Nowadays you can spit out most of your teeth in the port of Hamburg, the next day get shot up on the streets of Northern Ireland or be at the receiving end of a well-aimed kick on the plains of Greece. International boundaries are down. But let's face it: The unchallenged center of pure—one might say classical—violence is still legendary New York, city of jolly monsters.*

George, the Friendly Neighborhood Thug

When I first rang my Aunt Trude's doorbell in the heart of Broadway, her scared eye appeared in the peep-hole.

"Are you alone?" she quaked behind the door. "Is no one prowling on the staircase?"

I assured her that I was alone, whereupon Auntie turned the key twice, pulled back three bolts, removed the chain, temporarily disconnected the electronic alarm and opened the door, a loaded gun in her shaking hand.

"Quick," she greeted me. "Hurry!"

After replacing the barricade, Trude explained that only three days before they had strangled her landlord upstairs with a wet towel. We decided, therefore, that during the fortnight of my stay in New York I would not leave her apartment at all.

"I myself haven't left the flat for two months," my

aunt related. "Why should I take risks? Down in the street people are being murdered in broad daylight. You never know in New York when you'll be stabbed in the back. So we'll just sit here quietly, watch TV and cook gourmet meals."

It seems that you don't have to go outdoors even to buy food. Everything is brought to the house. But to play it safe, when a supermarket messenger rang the doorbell, my aunt opened only after phoning the store and confirming that this was indeed their man and not the Boston Strangler.

Still, I had to buy my wife a handbag. The little woman had agreed to my New York fun trip only on condition that I bring her a black lacquered crocodile leather handbag. For three days and three nights my aunt tried to talk me into having the corner leather-goods store send up some samples, but on the fourth day I sallied forth, hugging the walls like a furtive shadow.

It was fairly early in the day and New Yorkers were still dazed from the drugs they had swallowed the previous night. I passed a large number of drunks, shook off around a dozen whores and several professional monsters and made the bag store safe and sound. The plate-glass door was naturally locked. The lady owner examined me carefully through the glass, then rang Trude and double-checked. In the end she opened the door a crack.

"Sorry," she remarked, "but the other week they robbed the delicatessen across the street and crucified the sales girl on the ceiling."

By then I had begun to suspect that public security in New York had deteriorated somewhat. I quietly picked up that dream of a black lacquer crocodile.

"I have nicer ones," the lady said. "This blue bag with the golden clasp, for instance, suits you marvelously."

"I don't need a handbag," I assured her. "This is for my wife."

"I'm so sorry," the owner apologized. "Nowadays it's so difficult to tell who is a man and who isn't. Since you don't wear your hair long I took you for a woman."

It happened on the way home.

I passed three pornographic establishments unscathed, but at the corner of 43rd Street a giant, sloppily dressed Negro stopped me and planted his fist level with my nose.

"Hi," the man said. "Money."

I remembered the advice of the Israeli guidebook: In delicate situations abroad, always speak Hebrew.

"*Adoni*," I therefore addressed the huge Negro in our ancient language. "Leave me alone or else I shall become violent. What's going on here?"

And continued on my way to Aunt Trude and stumbled through the door excited and stimulated by the unusual experience. My aunt blanched as she listened to my report.

"Good Lord," she whispered before fainting, "didn't they warn you that one never resists them? He could have murdered you on the spot."

"He had no weapon."

"No need. They do it all the same. In New York you don't argue, you simply reason: Eighth Avenue, Negro, angry, pay! Next time give them everything you have! Better still, don't leave the house."

I left the house. Pretending that I had to confirm my El-Al reservation, I went out into the fresh air and walked the avenue quite unconcerned. On my way I

did not stop except in front of some movie stills to re-
fresh my memory as to how one makes children. It was
quite instructive, but on the way home, on the corner of
43rd Street, I was again accosted by the huge Negro.
This time he grabbed my coat lapels in an iron grip.

"Hi," he breathed. "Money!"

In such situations I act very quickly. I pulled out
my wallet with lightning speed.

"Why," I wheezed, "why?"

The Negro pulled me close to his face. He had a
flattened nose and bloodshot eyes.

"Why?" he said slowly. "Because you are a white
pig, that's why!"

The place had become quite deserted. Passers-by
ran for shelter and at the far end of the street two cops
fled on tiptoe. I pushed two dollars into his fist, detached myself from him and dashed back to the apartment.

"I paid!" I informed my aunt. "He took two dollars."

Trude again fainted. "Two dollars?" she whispered.
"You dared to give him two measly dollars?"

"Without a receipt," I muttered. "I didn't have
more on me."

"Don't ever dare to leave the house without at least
five dollars! Do you want him to slice up your face with
a switchblade? How tall was he?"

"Seven feet."

"Take ten dollars, for goodness' sake!"

On Thursday I slipped out to buy some foreign
pacifiers for my daughter. Around Times Square an un-
shaven individual tried to stop me for a onetime dona-
tion, but I dismissed him summarily.

"Sorry, I'm being mugged on Forty-third Street."

There is something like a double-taxation agreement. You pay either here or there but not twice. I continued to the corner of 43rd Street but did not find the giant Negro there. I was a little disappointed, having prepared a crisp ten-dollar bill for him. I looked for him in all the neighborhood taverns. Finally I discovered him at the entrance to a bar for nudist fags. He was sitting cross-legged, leaning against the wall, his eyes rolling threateningly.

"Hi, white pig," he snorted. "Give me more money!"

"Haven't got any now. We'll see tomorrow."

He didn't insist. Then I realized that as a matter of fact he wasn't all that huge. He was about my height, with only a few teeth left upstairs. On the other side of the street someone was raping a completely hysterical female and everybody was running for shelter. I said to myself: How lucky I am that George is so restrained.

"Ephraim," my Aunt Trude said a few days later, "you've got to see that Negro now, or else he'll come here. I know their kind."

I put a crisp new fifty-dollar bill in my pocket and went to our rendezvous on 43rd Street. No one molested me on the way. Even the pimps did not pull my sleeve this time, because they all knew that I was a steady customer of George's. He was waiting for me in front of a restaurant with topless waitresses.

"Hi, white pig," he breathed. "Did you bring the dough?"

"Yes," I said.

"Give, white pig."

"Just a moment," I said. "Is this a real mugging or only the taking of a certain sum?"

"White pig," replied George. "I need twenty-five dollars."

"I've only got a fifty-dollar bill."

George grabbed the bill, tottered into a hashish den camouflaged as a brothel for goats, and after a while came back and returned $25 change. I realized that he was playing it fair with me, so on the spur of the moment I asked him whether I could not take out a subscription, pay a weekly rate or something?

George did not quite understand. "White pig," he said, "I'm here every day."

I asked for his telephone number, but he did not have one. On the other hand, he showed me a rusty blade he treasured in his hip pocket, and for the firs' time he bared his tobacco-stained teeth in a friendly grin. Altogether he was a nice midget mugger, maybe four and a half feet tall, no longer young but very good-humored.

On the day of my departure, Aunt Trude saw me to the apartment door. She had wept all through the night at the very thought of my having to return again to the war, the bombs, the general insecurity in the region—but she had to agree that my place was with my family.

So I'm writing these lines in burning Tel Aviv. Still, why deny it, I miss George. We had understood each other. Between drags of hash, is he, too, thinking of his little white pig? I doubt it. Not everyone is as romantic as I am.

❧ *We returned to the site of our crime with the noble intention of presenting our satirical show,* Unfair to Goliath, *somewhere on the fringes of Broadway. The jungle closed behind us inexorably, the predators began circling and the theatrical struggle for survival was on.*

The Grave Robbers
of Broadway

The greatest asset of a show on or around Broadway is the theater itself. Those little halls are never empty. Productions line up to snatch them for kamikaze-swift suicide or dizzying success. There is no in between in New York. Either you scrape the skies or you close down on the morrow of the premiere.

It so happened that our own position was quite secure. The producer of our show—for brevity's sake let's call him Joe—had in his pocket a rental contract signed by the Episcopalian church, an official, almost historical document which placed at our disposal the theater hall in the church building for an unlimited period of three months. We had a cute stage; the atmosphere was intimate and puritanical. The rehearsals went their customary, madcap way.

And then the Department of Internal Revenue struck.

On that fateful evening our Episcopalian church received a circular from the above government institution, informing the church that in common with charities and the United Jewish Appeal, it would from now

on enjoy tax-free status only as long as it was "not connected with profit-making organizations." Panic gripped
the church. Not because of the tax it would have to pay
but because of the nightmarish thought that legions of
snooping revenuers would descend on it and start looking into the books of the church. Noooo!

Therefore one of the archbishops on duty called
on Joe and without further ado told him that our contract was null and void, due to an "act of God," see para
106 below. The world went black before Joe's eyes. He
fell on his knees and implored the Archbishop not to
destroy us. What's more, he brought up what he
thought would be a clinching argument—that we'd
never make any profits anyway but would bomb out just
like the other shows. He also invited the Arch to come
to the rehearsals and see with his own eyes that he was
not talking rot. In a blue funk, Joe also hired a clever
lawyer, who checked the contract carefully and declared
that there was nothing to be done since one could not
sue God. In the end Joe accused the church of anti-
Semitism, and when not even that helped as a last resort
offered to convert to the Episcopalian faith, but it was
no good.

It was therefore imperative to find another theater
immediately.

How do you go about that? Very simple. The interested party screens the list of forthcoming premieres
in the newspapers and tries to guess the certain flops.
There are also local fiasco experts willing, against a
modest fee, to look around town for flops, just like those
dogs trained to ferret out caches of hashish. The choice
of our team of experts fell on the well-known Corona
Theater downtown.

"Come," Joe said. "Let's go and see what's what."

We invaded the little theater through the back entrance, our hats pulled down over our eyes, our feet shod in silent gumshoes. Personally, I felt like a professional vulture hovering in the air on the lookout for a fresh cadaver, but such is life.

Onstage, the final rehearsals of a lively musical were in progress. Sprightly hoofers were dashing in and out of their dressing rooms, the stage designer was adding the finishing touches, the musicians were tuning their instruments, the director was shouting himself hoarse and the choreographer was taking the final steps ensuring success. We stood there in a corner, our group of grave robbers, and the expert among us drew a deep breath of air into his lungs.

"No," he said finally, his eyes closed, "it won't go."

This was good news indeed. Should the musical flop with adequate speed, this excellent hall would immediately become available.

"Say, what the hell are you guys doing here? Who are you?"

It was the red-eyed producer of the show. We told him that we had come by mistake, thinking it was a nightclub. We beat it, and, running around the building, we went up to the theater owner's private office on the second floor. That gentleman was slumped behind his huge desk, waiting for us.

He surveyed us languidly. "Hi. When do you want to come out with your hit?"

"Yesterday," Joe answered. "What's the situation?"

"The premiere of that hit downstairs will be on Monday night," the owner informed us. "The hall can be yours on Tuesday morning."

"Is that certain?"

"I'm ready to sign a contract."

"Excuse me," I interrupted. "Why must we wait until Tuesday morning? The premiere of the musical should be over by ten-thirty, so we could move in at eleven o'clock."

"Don't be silly," the expert scoffed. "They have to read the reviews first, haven't they?"

We shook hands with the theater owner, made a down payment on the dead-sure flop and left. On the way out we heard the gay singing of the hopeful players, as well as the pleased guffaws of the producer and his entourage.

Then we had a number of difficult days. We planted a man among the audience at a dress rehearsal and he reported that, though bad, the show was not actually catastrophic.

Joe blanched. "Good Lord," he croaked. "If they succeed, we won't have a hall, we'll be lost."

I proposed we poison the leading man before the premiere or sit behind the most important critics and prick them with pins during the show, but my partners called my suggestions infantile and rejected them. They put their trust in the press and TV reviews, since these never let down the average hall hunter.

On Monday night, when the curtain dropped on the musical, we were sitting at home in front of the TV set, our nerves frayed and fit to snap. The review on Channel 2 was lukewarm but not really murderous. On Channel 13 some idiot babbled that "There is in this mini-operetta a sort of winsome indirectness." What winsome, who wins, really one can no longer trust anybody nowadays.

Joe bought the *News*. Again the same thing: a panning, certainly, but nothing radical, no trace of the sizzling venom which bombs out shows. We were sitting there, biting our nails. If this goes on we won't have a hall. Our last hope was Clive Barnes of the New York *Times*.

At midnight Joe went out, his heart aflutter. We waited for his return, too dejected even to talk. Fifteen minutes later Joe burst through the door:

"We've got it!" he panted, beside himself with joy, waving the life-saving paper. "It's murder!"

One can trust Mr. Barnes in such cases.

The musical closed down that very evening, as it was supposed to do, and ever since we have been rehearsing on the stage of the Corona. It has a wonderful atmosphere. We are all full of beans and high hopes. Only one thing somewhat dampens our spirits: A mysterious group of men keeps coming to rehearsals. They stand whispering in a dark corner for a few minutes, then they climb the stairs to the office of the theater owner on the second floor.

What on earth could they be talking about there?

🌱 *I once paid a short visit, as amateur film-maker, to that factory of dreams (and a few nightmares), Hollywood. Though I am the proud son of the gay Mediterranean and my native country boasts a bumper crop of professional slanderers, the parade of Hollywood agents I encountered has left an indelible imprint on my psyche.*

The Brotherhood

You stand on the thirty-third floor of your hotel balcony quietly contemplating the famous Sunset Boulevard, which runs on and on and finally vanishes into infinite space just beyond number 11,935. The world's longest city, Los Angeles, is still the capital of filmdom, and if its studios no longer bear profits, at least they bear the imprints of Charlie Chaplin, Greta Garbo and Mickey Mouse. You experience a thrill: after all, this is the Vatican of the movies. . . . As your flow of consciousness reaches this point, there is usually a knock at the door. More often than not, a sleekly combed man stands in the doorway holding a small bunch of flowers.

"Allow me to welcome you to Hollywood, Mr. Kitchen," the man says, and hands me a cleverly designed visiting card, on which is engraved in gold letters: President, Cinemastro Corporation Ltd. "I was told you were in town," the President twitters, "and I just dropped in to tell you how much I enjoyed your movie. Congratulations!"

"Sit down," you say, a trifle excited. "Why are you standing up?"

"Do you by any chance know 'Deluge, Sanitary Installations, Haifa'?" Our guest sits down. "He's my brother-in-law, you know. So I thought it only right and proper, Ephraim, to come here and warn you: beware of the crooks in this city! They'll harass you, barge into your hotel room and tell you cock-and-bull stories about relatives in Israel, but as a matter of fact all they want is to be your sole agent for a fat commission. Come to think of it, what movie have you got?"

After a short but intense briefing, we parted on excellent terms. The President offered to become my sole agent for a fat commission, and I was enchanted with the idea, because I would have hated to hand over my film to an utter stranger. We decided to clinch the deal at breakfast. But no sooner had my benefactor left the room, than there was a knock at the door, and this time I faced an elegant gentleman sporting a slight squint.

"I hope you haven't signed anything yet." The man barged into my room. "I'm sure that son of a gun told you he's a Zionist and warned you against the crooks in this city. That's his gimmick. Then he makes you sign a phony contract, grabs your movie and that's the last you ever see of him."

I thanked him profusely for rescuing me at the eleventh hour from the clutches of this robber. My guest pulled out a folded contract from his pocket:

"I'll give you a third of the box office," he said. "Sign here, will you."

My ball pen was poised over the dotted line, but just then a black slave came in and handed me a cable:

"YOU ARE IN DANGER," I read. "AM WAITING DOWN-STAIRS. BUCHBINDER."

"Pardon me," I said to the third of the box office

and dashed downstairs. Buchbinder was waiting for me, hidden behind a potted palm.

"The gangster in your room is hand in glove with the 'President,'" he whispered. "They set up a partnership when they met in the prison for sexual offenders down in Alabama. He warns you against his partner and in that way worms himself into your confidence, and before you know what's happening he gives your film to the Sicilian Mafia. Those two guys have filled a whole cemetery in Hollywood. I hope you haven't signed yet?"

"Of course not," I scoffed. "I'm not as gullible as I look."

"I can see that," Buchbinder agreed. "What you need is a big and well-established film company that you can trust. I spend some of my leisure time as Vice-President of Metro-Goldwyn-Mayer. Where's the copy of your movie?"

"I'll fetch it right away, Mr. Vice-President," I said, overjoyed at this unexpected stroke of luck. But just then the hotel porter popped up at the other side of the palm and told me in a whisper that I was urgently wanted on the house telephone. Box Office, who, it will be remembered, had stayed behind in my room, was calling from upstairs.

"Hello," he breathed. "Has he gone?"

"Who?"

"The Rat. He introduces himself as Vice-President, though in fact he's a retired pickpocket. I bet he told you the President and I are working hand in glove like a couple of gangsters, right?"

"I seem to recall," I stuttered, "that Mr. Buchbinder did indeed mention something of the sort. . . ."

"Buchbinder is an alias; his real name is Kraus. He's wanted by Interpol as an inveterate debaucher of minors."

"How do you know?"

"What a question! He's my best friend."

I went back to the Rat and perfunctorily broke off negotiations with him under the pretext that the copy of my film was just then being washed and greased. I went back to Box Office in my room, my heart overflowing with gratitude, but the elderly elevator man stopped at the twenty-second floor and breathed into my ear:

"I sure hope you don't keep any cash in your room. Your guest is the king of safecrackers who escaped from Devil's Island only this morning and is now hiding in a whorehouse. Besides, he's a liar."

The oldster gave me his visiting card: "Confidential Films, Movie Distribution Company. Quick, efficient service."

I returned to my room on the thirty-third floor somewhat confused.

"Did the elevator man accost you?" Box Office asked anxiously as I came in.

"No," I answered. "Why should he accost me?"

"Be careful of him," Box Office warned me. "He's a notorious bigamist who pays his alimony from the proceeds of horse thieving. Hey, get a pen and let's finish that deal!"

The telephone rang.

I lifted the receiver. "Hello, I haven't signed yet."

"Thank God," somebody sighed with relief at the other end of the line. "Is that Bob?"

"No, Kitchen. Wrong number."

"Bob is a swine, keep away from him," the man said, and I thought, you're telling me? and hung up.

By now I was a little disconcerted by the professionalism of the softening-up process. I left the telephone and went back to Box Office, who had been rummaging feverishly through the clothes closet in search of the copy of my film.

"Routine check." He returned my pants to their hanger. "You're very smart to hide the film. This city is teeming with hooligans who wouldn't shy away from invading your clothes closet. Permit me to introduce myself, I'm Colonel Westinghouse of the Cavalry Corps!"

Only then did I notice that this was no longer Box Office, but someone quite different, with a red beard and a ten-gallon hat. They must have switched places somehow.

"Don't let the film out of your hands," the Colonel warned me. "This is a real jungle here, believe you me. You're sitting in a private screening room at the other end of the city with an apparently highly respected agent, an ex-officer, anything you like, and during the screening, while your back is turned, they remove the reels, take them to the laboratory next door and have them copied, without any fuss. Then they sell the stolen copies to Saudi Arabia and the oil sheikhdoms—they pay fantastic prices for a white film. . . ."

Fear gripped me.

"Are they all crooks here, Colonel Westinghouse?" I asked.

"Forget Westinghouse, that guy is one of the worst underworld characters, a dirty, cheating thief. . . ."

"Excuse me," I interrupted him, "aren't you Westinghouse?"

The Colonel fell silent and blinked several times.

"I'm a little mixed up," he admitted finally, "I meant someone else. They're all miserable pimps, grave robbers, most of them. They make me sick to my stomach. So where is your movie, Mr. Kitchen? I'd like to screen it as soon as possible in my private screening room at the other end of the city."

"I haven't got it on me," I said, choking. "I can't trust even myself."

"Did you hear anything?"

I pulled him over into a corner. Suddenly I felt light and carefree; the words just gushed out of my mouth.

"I'm the biggest crook you've ever seen," I whispered in his ear, "a congenital liar, that's what I am."

"Attaboy." The Colonel clapped me on the back. "Welcome to Hollywood!"

We shook hands and then and there decided to set up a film agency and cheat each other as much as possible. Since then I've been living in Hollywood distributing slanders wholesale. The address: "Westinghouse and Kitchen, Intrigue Mongering, 13,712 Sunset Boulevard." Entrance through the yard, don't sign anything!

❧ *No more stubborn institution is known to the world than that living corpse, American radio. New York TV alone beams from 5:00 A.M. till 5:00 A.M. on five wide channels, two of which are for religious blacks and one for the Italian underworld, and still the 103 small radio stations of the metropolis continue their fight for survival as legitimate media—as if there was the slightest doubt regarding the outcome of the ill-matched struggle between the brilliant color image and the wireless blah-blah. Small wonder then that every year a number of these ministations closes down, but not before they invite us for a last-gasp interview. As a matter of fact this is final proof that the station is finished.*

Oil and Fame Don't Mix

One of those wet evenings my Aunt Trude drew me into a corner somewhere in east Brooklyn and said, "You will never make a career in America unless you get yourself some publicity."

"I know," I answered. "Frankly, I'm worried."

"That's no good," said Auntie Trude. "You must appear on TV shows or something. You can call yourself lucky because it so happens that I have excellent personal connections both in radio and TV and I will fix up something. Though," my aunt added, "it will be easier in radio because I don't know anyone in TV."

The rest was child's play. My aunt at her hair-dresser's often runs into Mrs. Perle Traubman, who for the past forty years has been running the Fanny Swing Show at the Jewish radio station in New York—that is,

Mrs. Traubman is Fanny Swing and she has lots of fans among Bronx housewives and in moving cars. On that day, when my aunt returned from the hairdresser's with a new permanent, she told me the great news, her whole face beaming.

"Perle Traubman will see you in Studio 203 tomorrow at seven-thirty A.M.! I told her that you write beat poetry and are a colonel in the parachute corps, and she was greatly impressed. You are on your way to an American career."

We hugged each other, crying.

Mrs. Traubman-Swing is a pleasant lady in her sixties but doesn't look more than her age, except by a year or two, because of her blond hair and sensuous red lips. I waited for her in Studio 203 for half an hour, because she arrived just two minutes before the start of the live broadcast and proceeded right away to read the sheaves of paper the slaves had placed in front of her. Then we shook hands and she asked me, "In which synagogue are you a cantor, Mr. Freedman?"

I told her that at present I was not practicing liturgical singing. I was the colonel-poet Auntie Trude had sent from the hairdresser's.

"Yes, yes," Mrs. Traubman remembered, and her fingers leafed through the papers. "The cantor is coming tomorrow, if I'm not mistaken. All right, let's go."

With that a red light came on in Studio 203, someone pushed his head into our booth and hollered, "Go, Fanny!" and Mrs. Traubman instantly turned her voice into a nightingale's warble and spoke into the microphone suavely.

"Good morning, dear friends, this is your Fanny Swing from New York. It's raining outside, but at least it is not damp. Winter has come, hasn't it? This reminds me that we have with us here in the studio a very old and dear friend, whose name is known to all of you, I am certain, especially to those who pray at Or Kabuki Synagogue." Here I made a slight hand signal, whereupon Fanny made a sharp turn and continued, "As a matter of fact he is a great poet from Israel who is in America at present on a state visit as a senior officer and reserve astronaut. How are you, Mr. Kitchen?"

"Thank you very much," I answered in excellent English, "very well."

"I am very happy to hear that. How is New York treating you?"

"Very well, thank you."

"Have you visited our theaters?"

"Not yet, but I have a ticket to a musical day after tomorrow, and as for my own satirical show—"

"Lysczansky's Cooking Oil cooks by itself," Mrs. Traubman said kindly. "For light and nourishing meals, for crisp salads and for golden syrups, Lysczansky's Cooking Oil is peerless. What do you say, Joe?"

At our table there also sat a sour-pussed man reading the morning paper while sipping his coffee. They had introduced him as the station's political pundit and theater reviewer, but apparently he was also moonlighting as a spot announcer.

"It's the world's best kosher oil, Fanny," Joe now said. "Tasty, tasty, tasty!"

He smacked his lips ecstatically, then went on reading the alarming stock-exchange reports.

"Lysczansky's Cooking Oil is free of nitroglycerine," Fanny Swing summed up and again turned to me. "You write your poems all by yourself, Mr. Kitchen?"

"Yes," I answered, "thank you very much."

"A *gitn yomtov*." Perle Traubman smiled. "My

daddy always spoke Yiddish whenever he didn't want us kids to understand him. Ma also wrote poems but in Russian."

I could literally feel how my fame was growing by the minute all over America, including Alaska, thanks to the highly successful broadcast. Indeed, it is no small achievement to make the Fanny Swing Show. Some people would willingly give their eyeteeth to be invited. Auntie Trude told me that Mrs. Traubman had a rating of 55 percent in the shade and every word of hers is snapped up by twenty-five stations. In short, I was on my way to being a real star.

"As a matter of fact," I said, "I write in Hebrew as well."

"Isn't that wonderful?"

"Yes, Hebrew is marvelous."

"Personally, I don't worry about meals," Fanny allowed. "Lysczansky's Cooking Oil cooks all by itself. For crisp salads and golden syrup, only Lysczansky's Cooking Oil will do. Doctors warmly recommend it. What do you say, my dear?"

"Hell," I answered, "I've never tried cooking—"

Mrs. Traubman motioned nervously toward Joe, who rushed to the rescue.

"Lysczansky's Oil is kosher to the last drop," Joe said without looking up from his paper. "Don't cook for me with anything else but Lysczansky's Oil."

"Contains no nitroglycerine, is pleasant to the palate and easy to digest. If oil, then Lysczansky's," and with that Fanny again turned to me. "Mr. Freedman, where will you pray during the holidays?"

"I have not yet decided—"

"We'll all come to hear your cantoral singing."

"Please do."

"I am sure you will be a great success, Mr. Freedman."

"How can one fail with Lysczansky's Oil?"

"Of course," agreed Fanny, "this oil cooks all by itself."

"No doubt about it, Lysczansky's is tops," I explained. "What do you think, Joe?"

"Tasty, tasty, tasty," Joe improvised. "Kosher and contains no nitroglycerine."

I only smacked my lips.

Mrs. Traubman glanced at the clock overhead.

"Thank you very much, Mr. Freedman," she said cordially. "We were happy to have you as our guest. It was most enlightening to hear about Israeli cantoral singing, straight from the horse's mouth, so to say. A *gitn yomtov* and *shahalom*."

I put on my topcoat. "Crisp salads and golden syrup."

How do you say? A star is born.

❧ Doomsday in the jungle. The Supreme Court of pachyderms retires to deliver the verdict. Premiere! Pray, man, pray!

The Night of Long Knives

The official opening of *Unfair to Goliath* was over by 9:30. The show took fifteen minutes less than planned because the critics did not applaud, only the claque of relatives and friends. We too, the spiritual parent of *Goliath*, clapped surreptitiously, but the group of reviewers got up at once and left in a gaggle. They were headed by Clive Barnes of the New York *Times* struggling into his winter coat. Joe, our producer, claims that he saw him smile once in the first act, but Dick, the director, thinks that he was just picking his teeth. In any case, Barnes left much too fast. A cold wind blew down the aisles. Jerry Tallmer, the prestigious reviewer of the New York *Post*, had left twenty minutes before the end, his face livid with rage.

As he passed us in the aisle Dick had a seizure. "He's leaving," he groaned. "He's leaving, he's leaving."

I was beyond caring. During the intermission, when we hadn't dared move out of our seats lest we provoke the gods' ire, I had made up my mind to take the first plane back home and ask the government for asylum. It is said the airlines always reserve a few seats for refugees from Broadway first nights. I have a severe case of butterflies and can't catch any of them. Joe is the calmest, only he can't close his left eye and it blinks in the darkness like a phosphorescent button.

"Well," he keeps asking Bernstein, our PR man, "what do you think?"

"We'll see."

We hug the actors, not unlike early Christians stepping into the arena. We have only three-quarters of an hour left to love each other. The first TV reviews will then arrive and we will sink into limbo filled with primeval hatred. We all know the fateful ratio: Out of ten New York shows, eight close down on the day following the premiere, one agonizes for a few weeks, and one . . . Maybe . . .

Jerry Tallmer had left before the end.

The time is 11:00. We sit in Bernstein's office, in front of the TV set without speaking a word. Present: Joe and his wife, Dick, myself, Menahem (the young Israeli composer) and the seven actors. The announcer prattles some nonsense about Nixon and Vietnam and other quite marginal things. I am slightly bothered by the rushing noise in my ears; my heart throbs like a jungle drum. Actually, I am here only in the technical sense, for my tortured soul has long since been playing at home with Amir and Ranana. From time to time I mumble a prayer, that's all.

11:15. We stop breathing. Dick lies motionless; his hair starts graying at the temples. Only Bernstein puffs contentedly on his cigar (he is an habitué at funerals). In his hands he holds a small tape recorder to record the station announcer for quotable quotes. At long last he appears: Stuart Klein of CBS.

"Sharp . . . self-mocking humor . . . pointed fun."

Joe jumps up from his chair and lets go with a succession of guttural yells. We all clap our hands. This is how the Jews must have felt when Moses struck the rock and water gushed forth. However, Moses had better chances. Out of ten strikes, at least three are bound to succeed. We embrace, hop around the room and I send Amir and Ranana packing. Menahem levitates. Klein spoke well of us, Klein loves us, Klein is great.

"A hit!" Joe yells. "We have got a hit! A hit." He embraces me warmly and whispers in my ear, "I knew why I brought you over from Israel. I knew what I was doing."

I love him myself, because he is a good man. His wife proposed that I settle down in New York and that together we open a department store. But for the fact that the actors are Gentiles, we would by now be doing the *hora*. I can see in their eyes that they are seriously considering conversion. Should NBC praise us as well, nothing will stop them from running to the nearest rabbi.

11:20. Edwin Newman, the granddad of all panners, appears on the screen. Burning eyes are glued to his ill-boding pate. We are thirsty for praise, sir, lots of praise, with lots and lots of adjectives.

"Quiet!" Bernstein roars. "I am recording!"

Newman works according to the Chinese-torture method. He wastes most of the minute he is on the air on philosophical thoughts, on the meaning of humor and its purpose in the civilization of mankind. He is simply killing us. He knows only too well that we are sitting hypnotized around the set, so he drags out the passing of sentence. One frown from him and we close down tomorrow. As he comes to the end, we are more dead than alive.

"Altogether," Newman pontificates with sadistic relish, "it was a pleasant evening."

Joe collapses. Dick rushes out to fetch some water and fails to return. The actors fan their faces. We survived TV and are still alive. Now it is the turn of the three large dailies: The *Times,* the *Post* and the *Daily News.* Should even one be con, we close. (We don't mention it, but Jerry Tallmer did leave early.) Silence. Bernstein is trying to establish contact with spies planted in the newspaper offices. The *Daily News* is the first to respond. A nervous and muffled voice quickly reads into the receiver the marvelous—repeat marvelous —review of Mr. Silver, may he go from strength to strength. We are good-natured, witty, perceptive, fantastic.

Joe clasps me in his strong arms. "Genius," he breathes in my ear. "You're a once-in-a-century genius."

I believe him; he is the expert. The producer has a quick powwow with his friends. They intend adopting me as their son. Why not? We could talk it over. Dick takes a piece of paper and, in a shaking hand, figures out how much the swimming pool would cost in the villa he is going to build soon. Joe buys up the Empire State Building, a fleet of tankers, and even pays back some of his debts. I transfer my gains into the custody of the collector of Internal Revenue within the framework of a package deal which leaves me with mixed feelings.

12:15. The telephone rings. The *Times* spy reports. He has got the first two columns, filched at danger to his life, from the proofreader's desk. We are recording; the pulse beat is 103. This is Clive Barnes, folks, the Pope; he by himself outweighs sixty other reviewers.

"This is a nice little show, pleasant and heart-warming . . ."

These were the happiest three seconds in our whole lives. A miracle, that was the general feeling; an almost incredible Biblical miracle was taking place before our eyes. The Lord has chosen us to rule over the nations.

There must be something in us which disarms critics, radioactive, anti-panning bodies. My associates are building air-conditioned castles in Spain, complete with swimming pools. Only the experienced Bernstein is grim-faced. He didn't like the word "little." He knows why.

And then something terrible happens.

"But," the intelligence agent mumbles into the receiver at the end of those three happy seconds, "this show lacks panache and is too long."

"Lacks . . . panache . . . too . . . long . . ."

My heart stops beating. Joe blanches and grips his head. These four words have brought down our victory arch around our heads. True, Barnes added about a dozen compliments on my great humanity and things like that, but this is no longer the Song of Songs; this is simply an excellent review and that is not enough for survival on Broadway. Menahem utters strange sighs, Joe's wife bursts into tears, Dick's white hair starts falling out. And these are just the first two columns of the *Times*, and Jerry Tallmer left before the . . .

"What shall we do?" Joe asks his court PR man, and his voice sounds as if it came from the grave. "Do we close?"

Bernstein stares into the air. He rolls the fateful words on his tongue and tastes them for effect: lacks panache . . . too long . . .

"We could save a few good quotes from his review for the ads," he decides in the end. "For twenty grand it could carry on a few weeks."

He means $20,000.

The actors get up quietly and leave the room without saying another word. They are contacting their agents right away for new jobs. I feel terribly lonely. Amir and Ranana are back in my arms. Dick goes on suffering in a corner.

Joe stares at me out of his wide-open left eye. "They warned me," he barks. "They warned me against Israeli directors."

His wife motions to me to beat it before they lose their tempers. I go to pieces, turn into salvage. Menahem whispers to me in Hebrew, "The main thing is health." Stupid *sabra*. I hate Menahem with a burning passion. I hate Dick as well. He also hates me. And Bernstein. The PR man records the end of the *Times* phone call. Dick leaves the room; he doesn't want to hear.

"Excellent performances," the reviewer surprises us. "A very talented cast, very pleasant atmosphere."

Things start looking up. Joe collects his limbs scattered all over the room and gets up. His wife comes over to me and strokes my hair. The time is 1:30. May the Lord have pity on us. It all depends on Barnes's ending.

"I enjoyed a lot of it," the great Barnes ends.

"No!" Joe jumps up, shouting hoarsely, and drives his fist against the wall. "No!"

"What happened?"

"If he had said, 'I enjoyed it a lot,' we would have been a smash hit right away!"

Bernstein also opines that this little difference in wording could well cost us a million dollars.

We sprawl out, spent, on the carpet when a special-service delivery man brings us—for an exorbitant fee—the proofs from the *Post*. Nobody dares read them. Before us again appears the receding figure of Jerry Tallmer.

Bernstein lifts the proofs with a limp hand and looks at the review with knitted brows.

Eerie silence.

"Well," a voice out of the grave asks, "what does he say?"

"This," Bernstein says, "is simply a rave review."

Fireflies dance in front of our eyes, and I distinctly hear the chorus from Beethoven's Ninth. What a man, what a reviewer, this Jerry Tallmer! Others, those pygmies, have to sit till the end of a show, but an intellectual of his caliber knows at once what is good and what is bad. Of course he left before the end. That's only natural. What a man!

"My nose never fools me," Joe whispers. "I knew you would pull it off."

Menahem does not move; he must have died or something. We'll have to see about another pianist. As a matter of fact, no one is moving in the room. The kudos of the wire agencies and the round-up of the radio stations will find only our dead bodies. Joe slowly puts a hand in his pocket, pulls out the checkbook and writes out $6,000 for next day's victory ads. But deep inside he is crying. If Clive Barnes had written "it a lot" instead of "a lot of it" he would be practically a millionaire. Anyway the show goes on. My feet drag me outside into the dawn light. In the lobby I glance in the mirror and get a shock at the sight of the crazed gentleman staring at me from eyes sunk deep in their sockets. Maybe little Goliath has won, but his daddy will never be the same again.

❧ *Many of our national difficulties stem from the fact that in their time, all the installations of our ministate were planned for 500,000 inhabitants, half of them rabbis, while today we number—even at the height of the searing hot summer, when about a third of our people flee abroad—three million souls in the shade, including influenza patients. Our cities' streets were laid out for lively bicycle traffic, the ports for motorboats, and Lod Airport for the Haifa–Tel Aviv express train. No wonder then that from time to time we run into lots of snags which were not at all unexpected.*

Wide-Open Skies

Gusti was sitting over the console, reading a sports paper. Or so it seemed if you had peeked into the control tower. In fact, hidden among the pages of the paper was the brochure: "How to Control Air Traffic in 20 Easy Lessons."

"Better play it safe," Gusti said to himself.

Day before yesterday, after a real disaster had been avoided only by a miracle, he had almost got reprimanded by the Inquiry Committee. On that occasion an aircraft—it happened to be Belgian—failed to spot the power-station smokestack over the clouds and—*boing*— smashed into it. One of its wings dropped onto a twin-engined plane flying by mistake just below, but the pilot of the small plane kept his head. By a brilliant maneuver he landed on an airliner coming from Teheran, and both plummeted to the Bloomfield football stadium, almost killing Spiegel. Only ten yards separated them from the star player on the 16-meter line. Had the center forward's pass been a little longer, a real tragedy would have occurred.

Gusti looked irately at the big clock on the wall. No one had told him that this was not the radar, and up until the other day he had directed airport traffic by the second hand, which, it will be remembered, moves all the time around the clock face. As a matter of fact, the real radar had already been officially ordered in the U.S., and just as soon as the airport starts making money they would even get around to purchasing it. For the time being, a man was sent every morning from the Labor Exchange to the top of the Shalom Tower, from where he flagged down the incoming planes with a red rag. But this morning the Labor Exchange had again sent someone who spoke no Hebrew, and he kept signaling in Bulgarian.

"What a pain in the neck," Avigdor groused in another corner of the control tower. "That Pan American pilot has been pestering me for half an hour for permission to land."

"What's his height?" Gusti asked.

"Six feet in his stockings."

"Consult the chart," Gusti said, "and don't bother me with such trifles."

Avigdor started leafing through the instructions. "What do they expect me to do," he complained. "They sent me here yesterday just to replace Grinspan, who is down with the flu. It's only for a few days anyway."

"Have you completed a course?"

"Not yet. But you see, I work in a chicken coop, so they thought fowls, birds, planes—you know."

A tremendous explosion came from the runway and a column of black smoke rose heavenward.

"Oh hell," Gusti remarked. "We're going to catch it again."

He hung out the window the yellow balloon meaning "Be back soon" and went to have a snack. Altogether it had been a hard day. At lunchtime two big planes had approached from the sea and by mistake had intercepted the broadcast of a radio ham from Rishon-le-Zion, and since then they were circling Tel Aviv with their wheels locked, unable to separate.

Gusti had contacted the Siamese. "No sweat. Carry on circling."

"And what if we run out of fuel?"

"Let's cross our bridges when we come to them."

Gusti immediately called the Minister of Transport on the green line and demanded an urgent inquiry committee. In the meantime things had quieted down on the airfield, since the chief meteorologist had declared a go-slow strike, and only on the intervention of the state President did he consent to announce that the weather was fair. The driver of the hay wagon which had ambled onto the runway two days before was still looking for the exit. Avigdor rang his wife at home to ask whether there was anything on TV tonight. Someone cut in on the conversation and babbled something about lights.

"Get off," Avigdor roared into the receiver. "Get off, man, get off!"

"I'm taking off. Over!" the Air France pilot replied. "But something is landing exactly opposite—"

"I'll call you back later." Avigdor took leave of his wife and returned to the pilot. "What were you saying?"

"I'm on a collision course. What shall I do?"

"Watch out," Avigdor warned. "Be careful!"

Here Rishon-le-Zion came in and broadcast light music.

Gusti came running in from the kiosk. "The rain washed out the beacon on top of the tower," he announced. "Three are flying without lights at the same height. We'll have to act immediately!"

And without further delay he dialed for an ambulance and the wrecker truck. Gusti called Inquiry Committee HQ and asked for the van, so that the committee members should be present during the triple crash. But in the end only two met in the air. The third plane was warned off in the nick of time by a dentist who got on the line, and the plane landed safely on Ben Yehuda Street, corner Nordau Avenue.

The neighbors immediately started ringing the Minister of Transport.

"It's the second time this week," they complained. "We can't get any sleep in this racket."

The Transport Minister set up an inquiry committee. Customs set up shop on Ben Yehuda Street and began checking the luggage. In the meantime the two locked airplanes had dropped into the sea, but strollers on the esplanade thought this was an air display and cheered. The inquiry committee went out in boats. Rishon-le-Zion went off the air. The meteorologist renewed his strike. But as a whole, it was a quiet day, thank God.

One reliable way of measuring a country's true size is to check the standards of its television. Israeli TV broadcasts a mere three or four hours a day in black and white and mostly hand-me-downs. To those demanding better TV the authorities reply that there is not one single mention of television in the Bible.

Supervintage Wine

"Good morning, gentlemen. We are the purchasing mission of the Israel TV. We came abroad to buy feature films for our station."

"Welcome, gentlemen. We have a wide choice of films to offer you: action, science, war, love and 'crime pays.' In what kind of film is the Israeli public interested?"

"Polls show that they prefer films starting between eight and nine P.M."

"We've got them!"

"Just a second, gentlemen. We have to say right away that we are a particularly small country surrounded by enemies, therefore our TV budget too is most limited."

"Don't the Israeli viewers pay a TV levy?"

"And how, but the money is used for encouraging the textile industry. How much do your films cost, if we may ask?"

"Our prices vary according to the year of production. Films produced after 1960 cost two hundred and fifty dollars. The price of those shot after 1955 is only one hundred and eighty dollars. What are your financial possibilities?"

"Have you got something from 1930?"

"Naturally. Excellent films of Ramon Navarro, Gloria Swanson, the unforgettable Dolores Del Rio. It's like vintage red wine whose bouquet improves with the years. Here is a hit of the early twentieth century, *The Satan of Booze*, the U. S. authorities fighting bootleggers. Bela Lugosi in the part of the cynical moonshiner."

"How much?"

"Eighty-two dollars."

"Have you got something less topical?"

"Yes. Lionel Barrymore in *The Blue Angel*. Only sixty-five dollars."

"Is there a discount for underdeveloped countries?"

"Unfortunately, no. But an earlier version of this film with Emil Jannings in the part of the professor, of 1927, goes for only fifty-one dollars."

"Couldn't you make it fifteen dollars?"

"Sorry, this is a film every collector would give his eyeteeth for. Ask your grandmothers, gentlemen. The elder among them will remember this film. I am convinced that the Israeli public, with its exquisite taste, will enjoy this classic creation."

"It's a matter of budget, gentlemen. May we call Jerusalem and have a little talk with our bookkeeper?"

"Please."

"Hello, Zwanzinger? We found something most adequate, an almost new historic film, the price is fifty-three dollars. Fifty-three, yes fifty-three. Maybe we can squeeze it down to fifty-two. No, they don't understand Hebrew. That's the price, fifty-two to fifty-three. Still, it's a full-length, with all the trimmings, a director. . . . Excuse me, gentlemen, Mr. Zwanzinger asks whether you have an earlier version of *The Blue Angel*."

"I think so. From 1917, with Mary Pickford and

Douglas Fairbanks. An extraordinary movie. Lots of sentiment, lots of gesturing, maxiskirts—"

"Can you supply it from stock?"

"On the spot. I'll send someone down to the museum and within an hour the film will be here."

"How much is it?"

"A dollar and a half a pound."

"Hello, Zwanzinger? They've got a cheaper *Angel*. It's quite blue, perfect. . . . What? No, we didn't ask that. . . . Excuse me, gentlemen, Mr. Zwanzinger asks, is this a silent movie?"

"I guess it is. But with very clear subtitles on a background with drawings. It comes out beautifully on the TV screen. Accompanied by piano, of course."

"Mr. Zwanzinger asks, could the accompaniment be by harmonica?"

"Certainly. The Royal Afghan TV, for instance, gives drum accompaniment."

"Have you got something more classical, early Rudolph Valentino or something?"

"*The Great Train Robbery* of 1903, by the Lumière method. Forty-five minutes. Only twenty dollars."

"Tell me, gentlemen, was there cinema in the nineteenth century?"

"Unfortunately, only the zoogyroscope. A revolving disk and through the apertures you could see a racing horse or a ballet dancer in motion."

"Is it complete?"

"Yes. With kerosene lamps. Four and a half dollars including the crank handle."

"Mr. Zwanzinger asks if we could pay in installments."

"I think so."

"O.K., wrap it up."

❦ *There is an erroneous belief according to which politics is the only profession whose practice necessitates neither education nor experience. This belief does not stand the test of reality, because there exists another profession, though of a kindred nature, in which a person can become a hero of the gossip columns without any studies at all: acting. In order to correct this injustice and make it easier for the beginner actor to ruin himself, we concocted the following lesson after a particularly gruesome premiere.*

Who Says There Are No Small Parts?

Young man, as you are about to take your first steps on the boards, which means the world, you are definitely entitled to the sympathy reserved for holy madmen. We shall pursue your career with vigilance and hope to see you in parts suited to your lively talent. However, since the nature of your parts might well determine your very future, we should like to give you some pertinent advice drawn straight from the Mediterranean repertory.

First of all, young artist, whenever possible, try to play in flops. In present-day Israeli theater you will find everything: glory, satisfaction, intrigue, everything except a way of making a living. It is no secret that your main income will be from side jobs, from publicity shorts, from dance routines at weddings, et cetera, but for all of these you need free evenings and an actor who plays night after night in some miserable hit is in danger of starvation. Everyone gets rich on a hit: the theater, the playwright, the municipality, everyone, that is, except you the actor chained to his monthly salary. To say nothing of the fact that it is terribly boring to parrot the same lines night after night, in the same costume, on the same stage—why, it is practically an insult to your intelligence. Therefore, young artist, strive to appear only in bombs which get rave reviews. This is an ideal arrangement: to be praised by the press and then disappear quickly from the posters. In this connection we warmly recommend modern plays dealing with the lack of communication between man and man. They insure tremendous artistic achievement, but also plenty of free evenings for side jobs. It's a dream.

It is also desirable, young chap, to appear often in classical plays written in verse and translated with stunning virtuosity by famous poets. In those plays there is always a part or two not written in rhyme, and should you succeed in grabbing such a part you will be the only actor on stage whose words are understood by the audience. Your clear and outstanding diction will be praised extravagantly in next morning's reviews. In the beginning also try to do a lot of Brecht, because your pallid acting will be interpreted by the experts as perfect Brechtian estrangement. But for goodness' sake, stay away from any original play whose author is still alive, because chances are you won't succeed in "putting some life into those shadowy cardboard characters." An original play is a sort of domestic clash between the playwright and his reviewers. They have to come to some arrangement between themselves, and they don't need you for that.

So much for the play. Now about the part.

Stanislavski once said, "There are no small parts, only small-time actors." Maybe. It's a good idea to repeat this adage from time to time. All the same, take my advice: Play only in big parts, huge parts, parts with lots and lots of text. That is the main thing, lots of talk, if possible alone onstage, or with the others just listening raptly to your words.

You ought to learn to read between the lines, young man. Before you start reading the play—naturally only those scenes in which you appear—take a well-sharpened red pencil and draw a circle around your speaking parts. In the end count the lines and check whether they are sufficiently numerous and whether they are buttressed by intoxicating blocks of monologue. Don't forget that no lesser authority than Comrade Lenin made the remark that quantity influences quality. If you have to choose between a big but trashy or a small but good part, by all means take the big trashy one because it will do you a lot of good. Believe me, great actors always play leading parts. That is why they are great. Should you ever see Sir Laurence Olivier play in *The Brothers Karamazov* anything but a brother or a Karamazov, then you may change your outlook. Until then your motto should be: "There are no small parts, except those tailored for small-time actors."

Naturally, you should select with care the kind of parts you undertake to play. Never—you hear, never—take the part of a young, handsome, honest and rich man, who in addition—this is really too ridiculous for words—is head over heels in love. Such a part spells sudden death, a flop with the "f" in upper case. In real life one is either young or wealthy or beautiful or an actor, but one cannot impersonate all these up there without turning into something wooden and shallow, "a character who keeps alive onstage but does not bring the stage alive!" as the critics put it. Always play old people, young man, primitive and frightfully ugly folks, if possible with lots of weird deviations. In any case note the following: Beauty is amateurish, ugliness is always artistic, poignant. All international prizes are automatically awarded to the impersonators of madmen, drunks and sundry sex offenders. Now these are parts which give you a real chance to act. They have hair on their chests.

Here is another suggestion: Try to acquire some sort of speech impediment, a little difficulty over certain letters, a slight stutter, or, best of all, a trace of hoarseness. This will make the audience identify very deeply with you. Normal speech sounds quite unnatural onstage. Similarly, rags are always more interesting than smart suits and an infirmity is incomparably superior to good health. Be sickly, young man, racked with disease. A slight limp the length of the stage insures you good reviews in most morning papers. A shaking deaf mute is certain to steal the show. A drug-addicted, drooling murderer who escapes from prison on a dark night automatically becomes an unforgettable character. More so if he secretly has a heart of gold. A drooling drug addict who escapes from prison on a dark night in order to adopt his victim's orphaned daughter —this part will catapult you right to the top of Mediterranean theater. Though it must be admitted that a drooling drug addict who escapes from prison, adopts the orphan and then rapes her near the footlights is quite likely to bring you a grant from some cultural foundation or other in recognition of your daring. A drooling drug addict who escapes from prison, adopts an orphan, rapes her on the spot and then surrenders to the authorities—such an outpouring of morality makes the awarding of the Tel Aviv Municipality Prize a foregone conclusion. And if the jury also finds you not guilty as they sympathize with you—seems that the orphan really was a peach—and the outcome is a very happy end, you have excellent chances of getting a raise. Anyway, the future belongs to the monsters.

Always act the wretch, young man.

Nobody likes a big shot, everybody loves the underdog. Always choose the right profession, my boy. Whenever possible be the servant, not the master, a private and not an officer, a slave and not a slave driver. If you can manage it, try to be always a Yemenite tea carrier. An old pickpocket is also excellent. A sad-eyed peddler is simply out of this world. But don't ever be a normal happy and healthy person unless you have definite masochistic tendencies.

And now, my young and promising friend, let's proceed to a dialectic analysis of your text. It is absolutely imperative that you never forget the following ironclad rules. Never ask questions onstage, always answer them. And look for parentheses because they mark the fat parts. Don't you get the idea? Here, for instance, is an instructive passage from Schiller's *Mary Queen of Scots:*

MARY (*drops to her knees softly*):
    Indeed, the hour has come.
    Death, liberating and redeeming,
    Spread out your arms to receive me.
OFFICER: And what shall I tell the Queen, madam?
MARY (*rises to her full height, proudly*):
    To Elizabeth of England, give my sisterly
    blessing. I pray that she forgive the
    insults I heaped on her.

OFFICER: What else shall I say?
MARY (*with a subdued sob*):

> Tell her to forgive my death as
> I forgive her with all my heart.

OFFICER: Is that all?
MARY: Since you asked, my man,

> Tell my sister that I know she is but a tool
> In the hands of forces greater than she.

OFFICER: What?
MARY: Goodbye, go in peace, good officer.

> There is nothing left for me in this world.
> (*Climbs scaffold steps with her head erect. Stormy applause.*)

Got the idea now? Never be an officer, young chap, always be Mary Queen of Scots. Let Stanislavski play the officer. Therefore, no questions onstage! And remember, the fellows who play parts sans parentheses always take the first curtain call. Lots of parentheses, lots of applause.

Naturally one ought to remember that most of the time you are not alone onstage and this is most unfortunate. Instead, you are hemmed in by masses of other actors thirsty for applause and who could very well draw the audience's attention away from you. Therefore endeavor to play in productions with few characters. If ever you are offered a two-character play, don't even bother to read it—grab it. Another thing: Never be on the same stage with children, because they are so much cuter than you and each of them has ten mamas in the audience. And never—you hear, never—play alongside scantily dressed females or Yemenite tea carriers.

The part makes or breaks the actor, believe me, young man. Therefore it is understandable that once the repertory committee decides on a play, a gigantic struggle ensues between the actors and the management which distributes quite indiscriminately those fat, questionless and parentheses-studded parts. In this situation the best advice is of no help whatsoever. Here everything depends on your personal valor, Mediterranean blackmailing powers and proneness to hysterics. For a good part, wage all-out war against the management, ring up the director at midnight, burst into tears, be violent, cough until you are blue in the face, bring them a letter from your psychoanalyst, convert to Islam —but don't accept a small part! Don't surrender to the management—fight it. As a matter of fact, why shouldn't you be in the management?

Dyeing for Art

"Monsieur Boulanger, can you spare me five minutes?"

"Of course, mademoiselle."

"I was told by the theater manager that you are considering me for Desdemona."

"There was some talk along those lines, yes."

"I don't mind playing her. I read the play last night and I think it's not bad. Naturally, we'll have to cut Othello's monologues here and there, but you as director certainly know this without my telling you. I'd like to discuss my hair with you."

"I beg your pardon?"

"Look, Monsieur Boulanger, you came here from abroad and you can't possibly be acquainted with Israeli theater, which has deep pioneering traditions. We are—how to put it?—more conservative than you, if you see what I mean."

"Frankly I don't, mademoiselle."

"O.K. I'll put it to you squarely: If you think that for the sake of Desdemona's part I'll dye my hair blond, you better pack your bags and go straight back to Paris."

"I? Did I ever ask you, mademoiselle, to dye—"

"You didn't ask me because we have not yet talked it over! But I suppose you are convinced, just like those other morons—excuse me for saying so—that one can't play Desdemona without blond hair."

"But who said? . . ."

"I'm not interested in walking the streets under a radiant blond hair-do to stop traffic and make men turn their heads. No, monsieur, I can do without that pleasure."

"But who told you that I want you to dye your hair, mademoiselle?"

"You mean to say that you aren't demanding it?"

"Of course not. It so happens I like your dark hair."

"Oh, come now. It's horrible. Lackluster."

"It's absolutely O.K. with me."

"The question is, would Othello have liked it?"

"Why not?"

"To the best of my knowledge he was a black, wasn't he? It's hard to believe that he could fall in love with a brunette."

"Why not?"

"Because they are crazy about fair women. That's a biological fact. I always imagined Desdemona as an outstandingly Nordic type. But just for that, I am not ready to make a fool of myself."

"There is no need to, mademoiselle, no need whatsoever."

"No need?"

"No."

"I'm not joking."

"Neither am I."

"Look, you don't have to consider my personal feelings, Monsieur Boulanger."

"But I do, mademoiselle."

"No, no, after all you are the director and the show must go on and everything. If you visualize Desdemona with marvelous blond curls encircling her head like a halo, simply order me to go to the hairdresser and that's that. Whatever I feel afterward is strictly my own business."

"It won't be necessary, mademoiselle. What counts is character and not the color of your hair."

"That goes without saying, that's obvious. On the other hand, if you want me to identify with an authentic Nordic type, you'll have to stand on your rights as my director."

"But—"

"Here in Israel we theater people are great believers in inner discipline. We are used to obeying orders. When, for instance, we were rehearsing *Pygmalion*, the director made all of us sell flowers in the street for a whole week so that we should be able to identify fully. Before the premiere of *The Merchant of Venice* we traveled to Venice, and don't ask what we had to do before we played *Mrs. Warren's Profession*. The theater is a cruel world of its own, believe me. So if you really think that I ought to dye my hair, please say so now."

"What's the hurry, mademoiselle?"

"Because we shouldn't waste any more time. Yes or no?"

"Well . . ."

"All right, I'll obey. But at least don't force me to dye it platinum blond."

"Platinum?"

"It looks like a haystack, doesn't it? But for the Nordicness, I wouldn't even have raised the question. However, if it's a must, all right, it doesn't matter, I'll dye it platinum. What's the time?"

"Eleven o'clock."

"Thank you. Two hours from now I'll be a smashing blonde, but you know my views, monsieur. You have to excuse me now. I'm in a hurry, I've booked with Nanette the hairdresser. She's the best dyer in town. See you!"

❦ *"The spoken word is ephemeral, the written word eternal," the Roman sages declared ages ago, and today's yellow-press journalists heartily agree. Therefore the interviewee goes to meet the journalist feeling like the gladiator shouting, "Hail, Caesar, we who are about to die salute thee!" Still he goes to the fateful tryst. So did the gladiators in their time. Come to think of it, why?*

The Moth and the Flame

The deeply human drama we are about to relate started to unfold on that sultry Sunday when the telephone rang twice in Yehiel Shultheiss's house. At the other end of the line was a mass-circulation daily.

"Mr. Shultheiss," the editorial secretary announced, "Zila wants to interview you."

The functionary winced and almost dropped the receiver. This was the last thing he was interested in, because the shady affair of the Swiss francs had not yet been cleared, to say nothing of a few odds and ends from the time of his service with the overseas fund which were still under internal investigation. Besides, Zila was the acknowledged all-time bitch of the local press. Every week she tore someone to bits in her uncommonly lucid and ruthless column. Only a month ago she had written a profile of the university dean, and ever since he had not shown his face in public. What's more, he is said to be hiding in a photographer's darkroom because Zila described him as two-thirds reactionary and one-third homosexual.

Shultheiss felt that his last hour had struck. "I'll be

delighted to oblige," he said to the secretary. "When could we meet?"

"At the end of the week, in Jerusalem. Does that suit you?"

"Perfectly!"

Ever since that afternoon Shultheiss had not slept a wink. Formless fears chased through his mind: that Zila would write that he was fat and a crook and that he had hair on his chest. Anyway, this was clearly the end of his career. After the viper's disclosures he would be banned from civilized society. In the evening he was seized by a strange palsy.

"It's disaster," his pale lips whispered. "She'll ruin me."

"So don't give her an interview," reasoned Mrs. Shultheiss. "Must you give her an interview?"

"You know, that's funny," Shultheiss said. "That thought never occurred to me."

He was lying. Again and again the saving thought had flashed through his brain that as a matter of fact he could call the paper any time and tell them that he was not interested in any sort of interview. But this possibility was not technically feasible, because Shultheiss *was* interested. That is, he was dead set against the interview, since Zila would obviously tear him to shreds. On the other hand, he would have loved her to give him a write-up for the publicity value of the thing. This dangerous schism characterizes all of Zila's victims. It happens frequently that some minister or other grants her an interview and amid muffled sobs makes repeated and naturally futile attempts to grab her notes and flee. Psychologists call this "ideological split" and cure it with newspapers plugged into electrical outlets.

Shultheiss lived in the shadow of the deathhouse.

Even while shaving his chest, his lips were mumbling, "She'll finish me off, she'll simply murder me."

The receiver literally trembled in his hand every time he rang the office to ask whether it was all set for the meeting in Jerusalem.

It was all set.

Shultheiss almost collapsed with anxiety. Deep in his heart he had hoped for some sort of a hitch, so that the interview would be canceled. He locked himself in his room and practiced Zila-taming in front of the mirror.

"How dare you ask me about Swiss francs?" he hissed at his image. "Ask your shoes, shrew!"

He hated Zila with a passion and at the same time loved her with a truly adolescent love. He had a recurring dream: Zila chasing him in an armored car and then tumbling him in a flower meadow. By mid-week Shultheiss had visions. He saw himself in the form of two white mice fleeing in opposite directions. He also had visions of Zila.

"I'll throttle her with these two hands," he whistled in the noon darkness and added, "the tramp!"

His young lawyer promised to clamp an expensive lawsuit on Zila if the cheeky female as much as dared mention the dirty calumnies about those francs. "She'll pay dearly for every word in her yellow sheet!" the lawyer promised Shultheiss. It was agreed that he would receive his fee in Swiss francs.

The functionary literally shrank with fear. While sitting at the fashion photographer's for the pictures he intended giving Zila during the interview, he trembled to such an extent that all the shots came out blurred. Toward the end of the week, Shultheiss was seeking death. He drove at an excessive speed of 55 kph in a built-up area and tried to fix the toaster with his fingers and barefoot. On the last day he started drinking whisky, grapefruit juice, anything that came to hand. His eyes were red-rimmed and glassy with haunting fear.

On the eve of the interview, Yehiel Shultheiss showed up deathly pale in the kitchen doorway. "Don't let me go," he implored his wife hoarsely, his teeth chattering. "Tie me to something."

His wife took a stout rope and tied Shultheiss to the rocking chair in the living room.

"Even if I shout and rave," he whispered, "don't free me, darling, let me roar."

The woman stood the test. Right up to daybreak, the neighbors were kept awake by Shultheiss's yells as he abused his wife for not removing his shackles.

"Free me, you madwoman!" Shultheiss roared. "I want Zila. I want a big poisonous interview."

Toward morning the noise died down. Mrs. Shultheiss was awakened by the sudden silence and, filled with premonitions, hurried to the living room. Then she sped to the telephone.

Shultheiss had chewed through his ropes and fled Jerusalemward to Zila. He left only a few lines behind: "Pardon me, dear, I couldn't resist. Yehi."

The interview appeared on Friday under the banner headline: "The Return of Frankenstein" and featured a thorough analysis of the Swiss-francs swindle, plus the affair of the old belly dancer with the illegitimate twins, as well as a lively profile of the functionary spiced with epithets like "tubercular wart hog." It also mentioned the fact that he shaved his chest. Ever since Shultheiss has been a wreck who has lost his standing in society. He fell sick as soon as he read the interview and temporarily lost the faculty of speech. Mrs. Shultheiss did not move from his bedside, tenderly holding his hand.

"Why," she asked with tears in her eyes, "why did you do this, Yehiel?"

Shultheiss rose on his pointed elbows. "If I had the chance," he spluttered with a supreme effort, "I'd . . . do it . . . again."

With that he dropped on his back and closed his eyes and died to be interviewed.

❧ *Before we take leave of the various media, let us pay homage to the best program that the Israeli station succeeded in purchasing, or more likely was being made a gift of: the BBC series which conquered the world— The Forsyte Saga. Glued to our seats during those happy weeks of the broadcast, we became an integral part of that remarkable clan. The Egyptians made the mistake of their lives by not launching a surprise attack on us the night Soames Forsyte raped his beauteous wife Irene, since they would have found a completely paralyzed country. Or were the Egyptians, too, watching the saga?*

Spellbound

"Who's that?" I asked. "Is that the fellow who stole books from Fleur's husband?"

"Stupid," said the wife. "He's the cousin of Winifred, Mont's wife."

"The one who fell off the horse?"

"That was Frances, John's mother. Shut up!"

It's the same every Friday. We sprawl there in front of the Forsytes, even Amir, who should have been in bed long ago, and I always get entangled in the branches of the family tree. Last time, for instance, I had thought all the while that the painter of the new model was what's her name's son, until Amir set me right that he was Joliot Pere's cousin. Shut up!

Why don't they run the names as in the newsreel?

Look, now Fleur's husband is making a speech in Parliament, and I don't know whether he is or isn't the son of Irene, whom Soames had raped five weeks before. Besides, from the room of our new daughter, Ranana, there comes a suspicious noise and loud sobs. This is a real nightmare. Maybe our baby has climbed up on the bars of her crib and is now engaged in dangerous acrobatic feats. She could fall down any moment now. Terrible. Cold sweat covers me at the very thought of it. I could see that the wife too was laboring under deep apprehension.

"Who's that?" I asked her. "The young fellow who fell in love with Fleur?"

The telephone rings somewhere in the apartment. Naturally, no one moves a muscle. Anybody who calls a second time is simply out of his mind, puts himself beyond the pale; he is an abomination. Three weeks ago they brought us a cable or something and the messenger rang for a quarter of an hour and we didn't open the door. Because Soames was just meeting Irene in the matter of John's engagement or something.

"Quiet!" I roared toward the door. "Forsyte!"

Plonk! The noise of a heavy object falling to the ground comes from Ranana's room, underscored by loud crying. She has fallen out of her crib, our baby. What a calamity!

"Amir," I shrilled hysterically, "go and have a look what's happened, for God's sake!"

"What for?" my son answered calmly. "She's already fallen."

There you are! This bloody TV is more important to him than his sister! The wife almost cried with fright. On the screen Soames was arguing with a young lawyer.

"Who's that?" I asked. "Is that Helena's son?"

"Shut up!"

Now the noise comes from our bedroom. From

time to time there is the crunch of heavy furniture being moved and glass shattered. No, I thought, the lawyer couldn't possibly be Helena's son because he was run over long ago. That is, not him but Bossini, the architect, had died under the wheels of a carriage or something.

"So who's that?" I asked. "Is that by any chance Marjorie's brother?"

"She's got no brother," the little one hissed. "Look to your right!"

I waited until the picture faded out before the next scene, then threw a quick glance sideways. Next to my armchair a man was standing quietly, his face covered with a mask, and on his shoulder a large bag filled with all sorts of things. Michael Mont, Fleur's husband, was being beaten up by somebody in the Parliament washroom.

"Who is that who punched him?" the man with the bag asked. "Isn't that Winifred's husband?"

"Don't be ridiculous. He escaped long ago to South America with that actress," I threw at him. "Shut up!"

Poor Soames again came a cropper with the young lawyer, who bled him white.

"What this man suffers," the wife sighed in the darkness. "Everybody kicks him."

"Don't feel sorry for him," somebody said. "Remember how he behaved toward Irene that night. Who's that?"

"Shut up!"

By now two men with bags were standing there.

"Sit down!" I shouted. "We can't see!"

The two bent down and sat on the carpet.

"What's going on there?" the wife asked out of the corner of her mouth. "Who's that?"

"Anne's brother," one of the two men answered. "John's second wife. Shshsh!"

They kept talking to each other and disturbing us. The wife kept signaling nervously that I should do something, but I couldn't possibly move until fortunately there appeared on the screen the servant of the cousin of Soames's sister, a less fascinating old woman. I took advantage of the break, dashed into the kitchen and dialed 100 for the police. For at least three minutes nobody lifted the receiver. Then an angry voice came on.

"Sergeant's busy. Call back at ten-fifty!"

"Just a sec!" I roared. "Two robbers are sitting in my living room."

"Did Forsyte capture them?"

"Yes. Come at once."

"Soon," the duty cop answered and added, "Who's that?"

I gave him my name.

"I didn't mean you," Duty snapped. "See you!"

I hurried back to the saga.

"What did I miss?" I asked. "Is that Jolly, Holly's brother?"

"Idiot," the tall robber scoffed. "He died of typhoid in the very first installment."

"So it's a cousin of the nude model?"

"Vic, Vic, Vic . . ."

That was daughter Ranana quacking. She had crawled in from her room and was now trying to climb up my armchair. Outside a police siren was going. One of the robbers tried to get up, but just then Marjorie walked into the hospital and met Fleur face to face next to what's his name's bed. The tension had become unbearable. Somebody was knocking like mad on the door.

"Who's that?" I asked. "Is that the one who went to Australia?"

"That was Irene's stepfather. For goodness' sake shut up!"

The front door was broken down and crashed to the ground. We sensed policemen streaming into the room behind our backs. Apparently they lined up along the wall.

"Who's that?" one of them asked. "Is that Holly's husband, Val's wife?"

"Gentlemen, please!"

In the end Fleur refused to make up with Marjorie and went back to nurse Anne's brother. To be continued next week. It had been a marvelous installment.

"Fleur is wrong," the sergeant allowed. "Marjorie made a nice gesture. She should have accepted it at her brother's deathbed."

"First of all, Marjorie is simply a blackmailer, if you must know," one of the robbers said from the door. "Besides, he is not her brother. He is Bicket, Vic's husband, who had hired the detectives."

"Don't be silly," I shouted after them. "He went to the Far East two weeks ago."

"That's Wilfred, the poet, if you don't mind," the little one chided me. "Won't you ever learn their names?"

As if that were the most important thing in life. She herself had made a laughingstock of herself when, for two whole broadcasts, she had thought that Jolyon Fils had sold balloons on the street before he went to fight the Boers. She isn't going to teach me Forsyte, surely.

❧ *No use fighting historical facts: Long hair has become the dominant men's fashion the world over, and no one opposes it except parents and hairdressers. The parents protest because of the mystic connection between the length of their offsprings' hair and hash-smoking habits, while the hairdressers' concern is based on Sartre's existentialist theories. Tension is constantly mounting.*

Hair

The barbershop I patronize is perhaps not the most luxurious on the Mediterranean littoral, but it has everything needed for a successful haircut: three chairs, three basins and a bell that tinkles every time somebody opens the door. When I first caused the bell to ring, I was received by a senior tonsorial artist sporting a bald pate who pointed to an empty chair and said, "Please."

I put myself in his hands, but not before warning him that all I wanted was a trim, since I like my hair long and silky. The man nodded understandingly, and fifteen minutes later I looked like a Marine just out of boot camp. The barber's feet were treading my mutilated locks, his face glowing with the satisfaction of a job well done. The massacre over, the bald barber intimated that he was not the boss, pocketed the tip and we parted company. I did not really bear him a grudge since it was clear that the radical shearing had been prompted by an irresistible psychological urge. It was also obvious that his name was Grinshpan.

About two months later, when I had regained some

of my human aspect, I again called at the barbershop. This time Grinshpan was busy curling the hair of a politician, but another barber, a skinny and heavily bespectacled man, stood next to an empty chair and said, "Please."

Right away I decided not to experiment with him but to entrust myself again to Grinshpan the Bald. True, I mused, he was a shlemiel, but by now I knew his complexes and could neutralize them. Therefore I replied to the skinny barber, "Thank you, but I'll wait for your friend here."

The skinny one grinned cordially and tucked a towel into my collar right down to my hips.

"As I said," I repeated, "I'll wait for your friend."

"Yes," the skinny one said and bade me sit down. "O.K."

Grinshpan enlightened me: "He's a new immigrant," he whispered. "Doesn't speak Hebrew."

Then and there my resistance evaporated, since this was now a matter of immigrant absorption and the melting pot, and I am certainly the last person to hurt the little artisan just because he is an alien. So I surrendered to the skinny fellow and tried to explain to him in basic Rumanian that I liked a flowing mane, since I have beautiful hair, so it should not be shorn, only clipped of its unruly tips. The immigrant barber listened attentively. To my great regret he hailed from Poland. As a result of this geographic mishap, my head was quite unnecessarily shampooed and a torrent of eau de cologne swamped on me. I certainly would never have taken half this punishment from a veteran barber, but, as I said, Taddeus was a new immigrant and would have interpreted any criticism on my part as something akin to kicking a man who is down.

The third round started auspiciously.

As I rung myself in I saw that the new immigrant was busy parting the hair of an anonymous patriarch, while reliable Grinshpan was free as a bird. I quickly settled down in his chair, but just then Grinshpan slipped out of his white coat and said, "Enough!" He was replaced in the mirror by a brand-new personality: the third barber, young and Oriental, called Mashiah, as I later discovered.

"Please," Mashiah said. "Haircut, sir?"

The question of balance arose. As a matter of fact, I would have preferred Immigrant Taddeus to the Third Man since he had already proved himself a taciturn worker, but in the circumstances my refusal would rightly have been interpreted as bias against the Oriental community. I looked at Grinshpan for a stop-gap solution, but he had immersed himself in an evening paper, as if to say, "This is a cruel world, sir. Every man for himself." I realized then that though Grinshpan was accepting payment for services rendered, he had no legislative authority in the shop.

"I'm for long hair," I said to Mashiah. "Please cut it with feeling."

"All right, boss," Mashiah answered, and while relating his personal story, as well as highlights from modern Moroccan history, he left more hair on my head than any hick barber I had encountered in the past eight years. It was a pleasant surprise.

Early in April I came again, but realized right away that I was in a most dangerous situation. I found that though Grinshpan was busy working up a bouffant hair-do on a midget hooligan, newcomers Taddeus and Mashiah were idle and looking for prey. I wanted to turn on my heel, so as to avoid a direct confrontation between them, but I was too late since both rose and pointed to their chairs.

"Please."

It was a situation of unmatched tension, almost defying solution from the humanistic point of view, an eternal dilemma where one of them was destined to cut my hair while the other was left no choice but to throw himself on his sword.

I chose Mashiah.

The moment I sat down on his high chair I regretted my choice bitterly. Seeing that I had chosen the Orient, Taddeus winced as if he had been horsewhipped, though I assume that he had never heard that word. He quietly turned and made for the ladies' section. A little while later we heard muted sobs. I pretended not to hear, but it was an awful feeling. Now Taddeus would go home and his starving children would cluster around him.

"*Papo, dlaczego placzesz?*"

And Taddeus would answer them: "He . . . chose . . . him . . ."

Mashiah, too, was edgy and clipped my hair to the limits of utter baldness.

After this incident, I waited impatiently for my hair to grow, because I wanted with all my heart to compensate Taddeus for the stinging insult he had suffered. Before ringing myself in, I therefore passed the glass door several times and did not enter until I was absolutely certain that only Taddeus was free. I dashed in and made for the new immigrant's vacant chair—but inside a minimal kid had been hiding, and this brat up and took Taddeus' chair right from under my nose.

Mashiah stropped his razor with slow, suggestive motions, never taking his eyes off me, while Taddeus seemed to shrink and was visibly stiff under the effect of his erstwhile humiliation. Grinshpan, that snake, pretended to be quite unconcerned.

I waited on the bench panic-stricken. Who would finish first, Mashiah or Taddeus?

Should Mashiah again win me, it would be the end of the new immigrant, there was no doubt about that. It is rumored that at the Santa Catherina monastery there is a monk who once was a successful barber in Jaffa.

In the end Morocco won by a hair's-breadth. The kid in Taddeus' chair still had a few hairs on the top by the time Mashiah had finished his customer.

"Sir," he summoned me, "please."

I summoned up all my courage and said, "Thanks, I'll wait for him to finish."

Taddeus' face lighted up with unexpected happiness, while Mashiah tottered and grabbed the back of the chair for support. His eyes fluttered like a bird whose heart has been transfixed by an arrow.

"But," the poor fellow stuttered, "but I have finished, sir. What's the matter?"

Then Taddeus released the kid. We were left alone in the barbershop.

Quite a predicament.

Never before had I so clearly felt that man was simply a hapless puppet in the hands of fate. Quite possibly all this might end in murder, and nobody would be to blame, just as in a Greek tragedy. Tension rose to a peak. The new immigrant's lips worked convulsively, his nose twitching. If I took as much as another step toward Mashiah's chair, Taddeus would collapse.

Mashiah scorched me with his glance, the unsheathed razor trembling in his hand. He was suffering deeply. Grinshpan was counting money in the silence, his back turned toward us, but I noticed that his shoulders were shaking. His indifference was simply a mask. He had loved me all this time but had not shown it. A misplaced obduracy.

A strange weakness gripped me.

"You decide," I mumbled, "among yourselves."

But they didn't move. Only Grinshpan stretched his arm backward and with a slow motion opened the hot-water tap. Three pairs of staring eyes said, "Take me."

Perhaps I could propose a compromise. They should cut my hair as a team, or we should play a sort of Russian roulette. One would cut my hair and the rest commit suicide. Anything to break this awful, mute tension.

We stood motionless for about twenty minutes. Or maybe half an hour. Taddeus was weeping.

"Well," I whispered, "can't you make up your minds?"

"It makes no difference," Mashiah answered hoarsely. "You take your choice, sir."

And they went on staring. I stepped up to the mirror and passed my hand over my white hair. In a matter of minutes I had aged weeks and no solution was in sight. I burst out of the barbershop without uttering another word. I have never been back. Since then I am growing it long, hippie-style. Who knows, perhaps that's how this world movement started, in a barbershop with three barbers.

❧ *In our country it is difficult for a man to engage in sports. For skiing there is no snow to speak of; for ice skating the only ice available is found in the freezers of our refrigerators; gymnastics are boring; golf is anti-social and it is too hot for tennis. So all that is left is swimming. But the weather is too humid even for that.*

Careful, Shallow Water

My son stands on the swimming-pool steps and bawls.

"Come into the water!"

"I'm scared!"

For the past half hour I've tried to coax my little redhead to let his daddy teach him to swim, but he is scared. Amir's fearsome crying is still in low gear but going strong. One could say it's very promising. I'm not angry with my baby. I remember only too well how my daddy, too, tried to teach me to swim, and I stood there on the steps of the swimming pool and cried my heart out. In the meantime educational methods have improved somewhat. Far be it from me to force my boy to do something against his will. He'll have to take the decisive step toward the conquest of the waves all by himself. Like a royal eaglet leaving the parental eyrie for the first time, he'll need only a light shove. Nature will do the rest, even if it be a rotten nature. Understanding, kindness and lots and lots of love, that's what a devoted father has to lavish in such a situation.

"Look, look," I say to my kitten, "the water hardly reaches up to your navel. I am holding you tight. What can happen to you?"

"I'm scared."

"All the kids in the pool are laughing, playing, only you are crying. Why are you crying?"

"I'm scared."

"Are you stupid or weaker than the other kids?"

"Yes!"

Amir admitted this freely, unreservedly. A quick look around: The lifeguard is watching me from under his straw hat; scoffing parents are pointing us out to their frolicking brats. Before my mind's eye there appears a sinking ship, all the passengers waiting patiently in line for the captain's instructions, only a burly, red-haired man elbows his way through the crowd of women and children and plumps himself down in the first lifeboat. This is my son who didn't learn how to swim from his daddy.

"What are you scared of?"

"Of sinking."

"How can you sink in five inches of water? How?"

"I'm scared."

This child is allergic to water.

"Even if you wanted to you could not sink." I appeal to his intellect. "The body has a low specific gravity, so it floats on water. Look!"

Daddy lies down on the water and floats nicely on his back. It is most instructive, but just then some fool dives straight on my head and my mouth fills with water. I splutter, my specific gravity drowns, and my son bawls on the steps in third gear.

I enlist government help. "Mr. Lifeguard, tell him: Could anybody sink here in the children's pool?"

"And how," Strawhat says. "You bet!"

Any other daddy would by now have dragged his

son bodily into the pool, but not me, no sir. I love my son, despite his shortcomings, despite his inarticulate howls. What's more, I never loved him more than now, just because he shakes so much, because he looks so helpless, so stupid, damn it.

"Come, let's make a gentleman's agreement," I propose. "I won't touch you. You'll walk in up to your knees. If you like it you stay. If you don't, you get out and that's that. O.K.?"

My son bawls but takes a hesitant step forward. Result: doesn't like it, doesn't stay, gets the hell out and that's that. Amir is again on dry land. This time his bawling is legitimate. He also sounds muted shrieks and now and then yells "Mummy." That's his custom, to call for his mother in every situation, even when she's chasing him, fully intending to murder him in cold blood.

"Amir," I say to him, "if you don't get in right away, there won't be any TV tonight!"

Now that was too severe. My son bawls even in reverse. The pool water becomes distinctly salty.

"But look how simple it is." I demonstrate. "You stretch out your arms and count: one, two, three . . . four . . ."

All right, I can't both swim and count. No one ever taught me. I am not a swimmer. I am only a writer. Amir stands on the stairs and escalates. A fun-loving crowd has gathered around us. I jump out of the pool and my son flees for his life, his bawling at maximum volume, but I catch him in an iron grip. I drag him back to teach him swimming of his own free will.

"Mummy," my son cries, "I'm scared!"

I have a strange feeling of *déjà vu*. Yes, yes, my father too had dragged me like this into the pool and

I too had yelled desperately, "*Anyukám!*" Such is life; the clash of generations is inevitable. The fathers eat sour grapes and their sons bawl.

"Not water!" my son bawls. "Not water, Mummy!"

I'm holding him in the air about a yard above the water and he claims, crying, that he is drowning.

"One, two, three," I order, "swim!"

The child cries but goes through the motions. This is encouraging, but what's the use? I'm not trying to teach him to fly. I lower the eaglet cautiously to water level. He fights for his life, switches to colloquial Arabic, but I am stronger, because I am an athletic type.

"Swim!" I hear myself roaring. "One, two, three . . ."

He bit me! He bit the hand which feeds him, or rather the hand which right now is quenching his thirst, with his mouse-teeth he bit the hand of his father who has shown him nothing but love ever since he was born! I catch him between my legs and fix his shaking hips in a steel vise. I force his hands forward and then back, one, two, three. I make him swim, even if he drinks up the whole pool in the process.

"Don't . . . be . . . afraid!"

One day he'll thank me that I taught him to rule the waves. But right now he kicks. His feet, relatively free, beat a tattoo on my back, in time with his bawls. My son's face is distorted with crying. He has aged a whole day in just one hour. I push him deep into the water. So he's drinking a little water. Let him drink the Pacific Ocean for all I care. My father too had been held like this between his father's muscular legs. *Swim!* I can't remember when I last felt such anger toward any creature. What is he afraid of, damn it? What is there to be afraid of here?

The lifeguard taps me on the shoulder. "Sir, leave that kid alone, will you!"

This is typical. Instead of helping a father overcome the difficulties of teaching, instead of offering a cork lifebelt, instead of getting things going, this nitwit comes to the assistance of the noisy minority. I lift the eaglet out of the water and return to land, hardly concealing my scorn. My son stops on the steps and cries as he has never cried before, while I dive into the water.

I do an elegant swan dive to show the silly boy what he is missing. I use my favorite breast stroke, but something has gone wrong. It feels as if there is no coordination between my legs and my arms, as if I am sinking. Hell, what do you mean as if—I am sinking . . . Mummy! After giving just one lesson to my son, I have forgotten—forgotten how to swim.

Our Mediterranean sky is always blue, except for the winter months, when the weather becomes very nervous and changes rapidly from sirocco to an ordinary desert wind. Then a gigantic and endless struggle takes place between the washing hung indoors and the storm outside. The latest stage in the meteorological war: the sophisticated washing machine pitted against the automatic rain.

Heavenly Floodgates

I must admit that I have always respected heaven, but now I am literally afraid of it.

On that memorable Monday we awoke fairly early, glanced out of the window and said, "Whoopee!" The skies were as clear as a baby's eyes. There was no trace of cloud. A blue canopy extended as far as the eye could see. The distaff part of my family—that is, the little wife and her mother—jumped out of their beds with praiseworthy alacrity and said, At last. For ages now we'd been waiting for fine weather like this, so that we could finally launder the unbelievable quantity of dirty wash that had accumulated in a month of uninterrupted rain. The laundry basket had overflowed long ago, so we had taken to concealing our dirty linen in highly illegal places such as suitcases, under the bed and even desk drawers.

But now at last we had balmy spring weather. Wife and in-law pounced on the wash and in a matter of a bare five hours had it laundered down to the last pair of woolen drawers. Then we carried the wet wash—weighing a ton and a half at a cautious estimate—out into the garden and hung it on the antenna wires and on the balcony railing and on the fence and on the steel cable supporting the pole in front of our house on behalf of the electric corporation. It was an exhausting job, but in the end the last sock was suspended.

Then it started raining.

I don't know how it happened. Only a few minutes before the sky had been smiling down on us, there were no clouds in sight—and now all of a sudden it was pouring. Not only that, but it had become pitch-dark and clouds were converging from the four corners of the universe to hold their convention over our garden. We hastily gathered the wash together, ran with it to the bathroom and dumped it in the tub. For the last batch we had to use a ladder because the mammoth wash had reached ceiling height. Then we took a look at the paper and read the weather forecast—partly cloudy during morning hours, gradually clearing toward noon—and knew that the storm would not abate for at least three days.

It didn't. Outside, the skies dripped with monotonous persistence, while inside the wash fermented in the bathtub like so much Prohibition gin. By the end of the first day a penetrating smell of mildew-cum-graveyard-in-rain spread all through the flat and a green fungus appeared here and there on the walls.

"This cannot go on," the wife declared. "We'll have to dry the washing somehow before it rots completely."

We took a very long piece of string and started putting it up in the living room. The string set out from the window fastener, ran through the key of the sideboard, from there continued to the door handle and the mirror knob, then soared to the chandelier, dipped to the table leg, made a sharp turn and returned safely to the window fastener. The operation turned our living room into a replica of a contemporary sculpture. We removed the wash from the tub—so help me, it was wetter than ever —and suspended it from the abstract line I have just described. Then we lighted the kerosene heater to speed the drying process, and life returned to normal. Except that every time we crawled on our bellies, combat-fashion, through the living room, we got soaked, both from the puddles on the floor and from the water dripping down from the suspended clothes. The little one's mother declared that a bat would be able to fly between lines like ours without bumping into them, because it is fitted with a kind of natural radar, but that intelligence was of only marginal interest to me, since I'm not a bat.

At exactly 1:35 P.M. we heard a sharp report coming from the living room, something like *pinggg!* The house shuddered and settled gently on its side. Shouting hoarsely, we dashed to the resting place of our laundry to find utter chaos. The string, having decided that after all it was of local manufacture, had snapped near the mirror knob. The monstrous load had thereupon crashed to the floor, where it lay prostrate like Gulliver captured by the Lilliputians.

"Take it easy," my heroic wife said, although she herself was on the verge of collapse. The family council met and declared a state of emergency, and we mobilized all our resources in an all-out effort to gather the wash and spread it on tables and chairs and cupboards and mantelpieces. After a two-hour combined effort we succeeded in covering the last upright object in the place and collapsed on the wet floor in a state of complete exhaustion.

Then there was a knock at the door.

A funereal mood gripped us. My mother-in-law tip-toed to the window and peered out. "Dr. Zatopekski, the Supreme Court Justice and his wife," she whispered through trembling lips. We almost fainted with embarrassment. Dr. Zatopekski calls on us about once in five years and we consider his visits a signal honor. But on this particular occasion we would willingly have dispensed with the honor.

It is such dangerous situations that separate the boys from the men. The little one was the first to recover and issued orders in the following clear language: "Quick! Let's move the wash to the bedroom. In the meantime, one of you keep them at the door."

As the only writer in the family I am considered the most accomplished liar of all, so I was assigned the latter task. I opened the door wide, greeted the Justice and his lady cordially and expounded in minute detail the qualities of the plastic paint covering the entrance walls, hoping to drown the noise of scurrying feet coming from inside, until Mrs. Zatopekski remarked plaintively that she would like to sit down. Then came the whistle that signaled "It's O.K. now." We went into the living room and sat down. While my mother-in-law was asking the guests, "Tea, coffee, cocoa?" the little one whispered in my ear that they had fortunately managed to pile the wash on the sofa, though it was dripping horribly.

My mother-in-law tottered out to make some cocoa and collapsed in the kitchen doorway with a most disturbing noise, while we chatted amiably with Dr. Zatopekski about strange cases he had handled lately. Suddenly we noticed a recurrent noise originating in the room itself. We fell silent and in the deep quiet found that Mrs. Zatopekski's teeth were chattering rhythmically.

"Your ch-ch-chairs are te-te-terribly cold," the unfortunate woman whispered, and as she rose from her seat we noticed a big wet stain spreading on the bottom of her dress, while on her back was a thin layer of bluish algae. Then we realized that, as a matter of fact, we were all of us shivering with wet and cold.

"The humidity of this room is quite extraordinary," Dr. Zatopekski declared and sneezed three times in rapid succession, but we just tittered nervously and replied that this was only an illusion; our room was no different from any other room—and then something awful happened.

Suddenly there appeared under the door a tongue of water which advanced rapidly and in a few seconds was lapping at the carpet. The secret of the adjoining room visibly depressed the learned judge and his wife, and they informed me that they had to make another call and must go now.

"What's the hurry? Stay a while longer," the little woman stuttered, her feet splashing in running water, but the Zatopekskis left, greatly alarmed, and I really cannot blame them. By the time my mother-in-law brought the cocoa the desperate rescue operation was in full swing. I acted as a sort of Aswan High Dam, trying to stem the flood and turn it back with a broom, while the wife did the mopping-up operation.

When the job was finished at last my tortured glance swept the mountain of laundry on the sofa and an irresistible attack of nausea gripped me. Without another word I gathered up the wash, rushed out in the pouring rain and hung it all up again on the antenna, the railing, the fence and the electric corporation cable.

Ever since it has been doing a sort of St. Vitus dance out there in the rain—but peace and quiet reign in our house. We'll wait until everything dries once the weather improves. Then we'll burn it.

🌸 *It seems that the toy industry has been marking time for dozens of years. Always the same electric train running around in maddening circles, the same dolls prattling in Italian and the chipped dominoes last used in the fall of 1927. Toy manufacturers simply do not understand that in keeping with the spirit of their time, present-day children are interested only in two kinds of toys: those conducive to organized havoc and those which appeal to the hoarding instinct.*

Following is a rare sample of a dual-purpose toy; it gives satisfaction to the hoarding kid and at the same time plays havoc with his parents.

A Brontosaurus in
Every Drawer

A few months ago an unknown genius discovered that nowadays kids are no longer willing to look at picture books unless they have to glue in the pictures themselves and can leave the glue on the carpet. This brainstorm resulted in the album which is lately wrecking the majority of the country's marriages. Called "This Marvelous World," it features forty-six pages and on every page nine colored pictures which you have to buy at Mrs. Frish's next to the laundry, three pictures for five pennies.

The album is highly educational, its pictures covering all the marvels of the world, living and inanimate, the solar system and prehistoric monsters, all in a nutshell from the Pyramids to the most up-to-date rotary presses with a capacity of 100,000 pictures ready for glueing.

The presses work twenty-four hours a day.

For my son Amir.

The main gimmick of the educational campaign is that pictures are sold in closed envelopes and the brat buying from Mrs. Frish gets lots and lots of chaff before he finds the missing grain. While undermining the parents' financial status, the operation encourages bright children to think of a stock-market career as they trot to school lugging their little valises with hundreds of thousands of pictures for swapping.

Trouble is that Amir has practically cornered the market. For about six months now this smart kid has been investing all his savings in pictures. His room is ankle-deep in world marvels, and you can't open a drawer without at least a dozen brontosauruses tumbling out.

"Son," I said to Amir once, "your album is already bursting with marvels. Why do you buy more pictures?"

Amir lowered his eyes and answered, "Just in case."

In his favor be it said that he has not the faintest idea what he is glueing in, since he does not bother to read the captions. What he knows, for instance, about centrifugal force is that Gili gave him two swordfishes for it and a Messerschmitt 109. It's simply a case of overkill, a syndrome greater powers than Amir also indulge in.

Amir also steals.

I discovered this one afternoon as I half opened an eye during my midday nap and found my red-haired offspring dipping his hand into the hip pocket of my trousers.

"Hey!" I awoke with a jerk. "What are you doing there?"

"Looking for money," my son answered simply. "Gili hasn't got look-through sea stars."

"And," I raised my voice, "can't Gili steal from his own daddy?"

"No. His daddy is nervous."

That stood to reason. I consulted my wife, the delinquent's mother, and jointly we decided against emigration, since the album would follow us everywhere. Instead, we called an emergency meeting of the PTA with the participation of Teacher Hemda, who estimates the amount of pictures in the possession of her pupils at three to four million per class.

"There is only one way out," Teacher Hemda opined, "and that is to draw the income-tax people's attention to the excessive profits enjoyed by the manufacturers."

I disclosed to them that Amir was stealing. They only laughed.

"My son carried out an armed robbery the other day," a miserable parent informed us. "The child tried to murder his grandfather with a hammer, only because he wouldn't give him money to buy pictures."

The grandfather is fine. Several parents proposed a global ban on the manufacture of glue, at least for a few months, while one of those present, by the name of Frish, recommended the Danish system, which succeeded so well in the war against pornography. In other words, one should buy the child so many pictures that he becomes surfeited with them. We accepted this as an interim measure. Next day I bought Amir a whole basketful of new pictures, among them the terrifying "Victims of the Aztecs" and Leonardo's "First Airplane."

The kid absorbed the basket with the greatest of ease. Though in acceding to our urgent request he scattered the latest shipment over the whole of our basement. Only the other week our pediatrician, looking for a spoon, opened the top locker of our kitchen cupboard and was buried alive under an avalanche of this marvelous world. The doctor is fine. Right now the whole household has switched over to the Danish way of life. The toilet is clogged with dinosaurs and every morning I grab a shovel and clear a narrow path through the pictures to our doorway. The album itself has long since disappeared under those marvelous mountains, and still the kid clamors for more.

Even his looks have altered. His eyes have narrowed, his face has widened in a horizontal direction. According to my wife he is gradually turning into a hamster.

Yesterday I locked myself in my study. I swept away a bit of mythology and sat down to read the paper. And then I felt somebody lightly stroking my hair.

My hamster-son faced me, in his hands a little hoard of black-and-white photos.

"Giora Spiegel." He showed me a dozen likenesses of the popular football star. "I've also got twenty-one Peles and Bobby Moores."

The World of Sport had arrived. The competing album.

And this is where I take leave of my faithful readers. I enjoyed writing for you over the years. Thanks for your attention. Should we not meet again, please look for my body in the living room, right under two halfbacks and a goalkeeper.

❧ *In discussing the sex revolution which is slowly destroying us, we are referring first and foremost to the miniskirt, because all the rest devolves from it. This frugal dress has given new content to men's lives. Indeed, for the first time in the history of mankind the average married man, with his very limited maneuverability, is enabled to see something legally and in a dignified way. Men, who for years had not left the family kennel, now stream out into the main thoroughfares where they roam until exhaustion, eyes lowered, or else they dig in at exposed café window observation posts and from there launch low-trajectory glances in all directions, leaving their chairs with hard feelings.*

The advantages of the mini are too numerous for all to be mentioned here. Tanned thighs are a powerful come-hither, more people are getting married, even more are divorcing, the turnover increases. Women liberated themselves from the slavery of high heels, and whole branches of industry flourish due to the mini's beneficial influence—for instance garages, because of the difficulty of driving with one's head turned around, etc. The reader will have to excuse us for being so long-winded, but in our view the mini is the century's most important invention.

Lament for a Fallen Hemline

In our closest family circle, the little woman followed the dictates of fashion obediently. Enjoying our

fullest moral support, she shortened her skirt by half—
and the end was not yet in sight. We kept encouraging
her.

"Even if your legs are not perfect," we said to her,
"they are certainly a conversation piece."

She snipped off half an inch here, another half
there. Those were happy times.

And then the party poopers struck.

As always, the trouble was started by the industrial-
financial complex. The outlook for clothing manufacturers was glum. The world has a population of three
billion, of whom half are women. If we deduct from
these infants and Prime Ministers, that still leaves at
least a billion consumers, each of whom possesses two
and one half skirts. (True, in Socialist countries women
have only one skirt, but my wife is restoring the global
average.) Therefore, the loss to the textile industry
amounts to two and a half billion meters per annum.

Cloth manufacturers don't give a damn about
beauty. In their eyes money comes before morals. They
met in a dark Paris alleyway for an emergency summit
and secretly decided to lower skirts to the floor.

"This should compensate us for losses during the
past few years," the *capo mafiosi* summed up and added,
"but what about Kishon? This will be the end of him."

"Never mind," a Belgian manufacturer replied.
"Our profits are all that matters."

Disgusting. That is the only word to describe the
worldwide reaction to the Mafia's ruling. Women,
among them elderly broads with Army-age sons, were
not ashamed to lengthen their skirts to the floor. Naturally, the back-room boys at Mafia headquarters had seen
to it that the process should be gradual. They applied
the infamous salami tactics; every week an inch or so.

The little woman wholeheartedly shared my revulsion.

"They've gone completely mad," she flared up. "Surely they don't expect us to change our whole wardrobe."

Yet, somehow, I had a feeling that her hemline had dropped somewhat.

"Come on," the little woman scoffed. "This is the 'double mini,' the latest rage."

Let it be mentioned in passing that the shortening process is entirely different from its counterpart, lengthening. All you need for the former is a pair of scissors. Fo the latter only a new skirt will do.

It is against this background that the reader should envisage how upset I was when, early this summer, we set out, the wife and myself, for an evening of parapsychology with a medium from abroad. I stood rooted to the doorstep. An alarm bell clanged in my brain: the wife's bright red skirt almost reached the kneeline.

"Woman," I snorted, "you are lengthening!"

"You're crazy. I swear I didn't add a single inch."

Suspecting the worst, I stepped up to her and with a slow motion raised her sweater. It was just as I had thought: She had lowered her mini to hipline, cowboy-style, thereby turning it into a potential bikini. Her obvious surrender to the clothes Mafia enraged me, but she stubbornly repeated that this was a cute new "low mini," and I need not worry ; no expense was involved.

"Woman," I roared, "this is not a matter of money but of *joie de vivre!*"

In the end we compromised and reached an agreement: The "red line" would be three centimeters above the knee. Naturally, I increased my vigilance regarding the implementation of the agreement, and this was a wise step indeed. One evening in June we left home for another dose of parapsychology, and lo and behold, the wife's skirt was on a level with her knees. Clearly, the foxy creature was moving the rockets eastward.

I demanded an immediate explanation.

"I don't know what's going on here," the woman mumbled. "Maybe my knees are rising."

She repeated her pledge not to change the status quo even under pressure from sundry Mafia-sponsored fashion magazines. If some Paris fashion-designer queer decrees ankle-length skirts, he can wear them, but we won't waste money on unnecessary changes in fashion, right? As a matter of fact, the wife opined, the midi is simply revolting, neither fish nor fowl.

"Take my word for it," the woman reassured me, "I'm nobody's fool!"

In the middle of July we were on our way to some more para, when I was overcome by a strange sensation. The woman's knees had disappeared completely; so had her feet. She had trespassed the border in broad daylight and in blatant disregard of our agreement. Also, she had grown so tall that I had to peek under her skirts to make sure she was not walking on stilts.

"What's this?" I hissed. "What's this?"

"Nothing. Leave me alone."

I did not say another word but placed a twenty-four-hour tail on her. On that dark night I opened one eye and the woman was not lying next to me.

I crept out of the bedroom. After a short while the little one appeared on the kitchen doorstep with a tray and started down the basement stairs. I followed her on tiptoe and stopped in the entrance.

Goodness!

At one end of the basement stood an ancient sewing machine, and bent over it was an old crone of a seamstress, with dozens of skirts scattered all over the place, skirts and trousers, and all of them long, long, long.

"So this is it," I roared. "Maxis!"

The old seamstress jumped up and started packing the loot in a panic. She was used to such scenes in the north of Tel Aviv. The little one cowered against the furnace-room wall.

"Yes!" she moaned, her eyes protruding in their sockets. "Yes, maxis! All my dresses are maxi, down to the floor, or even lower. I want a train—two meters, three. Always maxis. They're cute. I hate minis, always hated . . . only maxis, *maxis!*"

She burst into hysterical sobs and fell on the water boiler. Without another word I turned on my heel and left her. She is no different from all the others, a spineless puppet in the hands of the Mafia. This is the end.

❧ *Woman's soul is an open book to the author, but unfortunately this best seller is written in a totally unintelligible language. Why are women the way they are? King Solomon, an internationally recognized expert on the weaker sex, carried out an extensive survey among his thousand wives and in the end reached the inevitable conclusion: vanity, vanity, all is vanity. The King has spoken.*

The Swivel Syndrome

No one can deny that man has achieved tremendous progress on earth. Since he started walking upright, man succeeded in subduing the forces of nature. He invented the zipper and solved the mysteries of Creation, including those of outer space. Only in one field has he failed dismally, one extrasensory phenomenon he will never be able to control: women turning around.

Because they do, especially my little wife. Whenever we are sitting in a place of public entertainment, be it a café, sports stadium or cinema, and I spot behind the woman's back people I don't want to recognize in any circumstances, I only have to whisper to her, "The Zeligs just came in. Don't turn around!"

And she immediately turns around. At once, without a moment's hesitation, in the most conspicuous way possible. She stares at the Zeligs with wide, guileless eyes and I sink into the ground, terribly embarrassed. (Apparently they are getting divorced.) After such incidents I find myself foaming at the mouth, and I try to explain to the wife that an adult person . . . After all, what's going to happen if we can't . . . and that there are delicate situations where one definitely . . . whereupon the little woman answers that nothing really has happened; the Zeligs had not noticed her at all. The hell they hadn't. Zelig had hardly come in when he demonstratively turned his back on us and only his wife had given us a long glance, though Zelig had probably implored her not to turn around. Anyway, now they know that we spoke about them and that's most unpleasant.

But there is nothing one can do in this matter. One might as well talk to the walls; it's a cry in the wilderness. Time and again I practically drop on my knees as I beseech my spouse, "Under no circumstances, you hear," I hiss at her behind my hand, "under no circumstances, please, under no circumstances, don't you . . ."

By then she has turned around, her inquisitive eyes gaping at the people I didn't want to look at. She always spots them by a sort of built-in radar. This state of havoc has been going on for years now. From time to time I resort to desperate tricks—for instance, while warning her, "Don't turn," I look furtively to the right when as a matter of fact Siegler, who owes me I£2,000, has just come in on the left, so the wife immediately looks left and Siegler knows that I mentioned his debt. It's so unpleasant.

Some time ago I consulted a psychiatrist. I described the situation in all its seriousness. He understood me only too well.

"My wife also swivels," he confessed. "It's an awful legacy dating way back to the Tree of Knowledge. It expresses itself in a morbid lust to break the Commandments. We all remember the story of Lot's wife. He implored her, 'Don't look around!' The rest is history. Women! But it seems there is a simple remedy: Instead of prohibiting, you should explicitly command her to turn around."

That made sense. Last night, in one of the restaurants, I applied the preventive method. As soon as Bar-Honig, who had embezzled I£100,000 and was now having a tough time in court, came in I addressed the little woman: "Quick, turn around!" I threw at her. "Bar-Honig just came in!"

She turned around at once and rested her eyes searchingly on the shaken man. I almost died of shame. I think I'll travel down to Sodom and check that pillar of salt. I have a feeling that it is actually Mr. Lot.

Maximalists' Revolt

Like all serious things, it all started with a toothache. The dentist found that there was a hole in one of my molars, but in the middle of the treatment he turned off the drill and slipped out of his white smock.

"Sorry," he said. "It's not worth my while continuing."

I lay supine in his chair, my mouth pried wide open by a little springy instrument, groaning dejectedly.

"My net income reached I£1,000 a month this year," he said, and started stacking his instruments in their cabinet. "I am paying maximum tax at the rate of over eighty percent on every additional pound. It is not worth the trouble."

I motioned with my hands that I was for continuing the treatment regardless.

"It's not worth your while either, sir," the dentist coaxed me. "You have to earn I£3,000 to keep I£600 net with which to pay me. And after paying tax on that sum I'll be left with only I£120. I intended to pay this I£120 to my wife's driving teacher. In other words, out of your I£3,000 the teacher will actually get a total of I£24."

"All right," I said, "but that's net!"

"True," the dentist agreed, "but unfortunately our driving teacher doubled his fee as of yesterday and now asks I£48 net per lesson. So, to pay him the extra I£24 I now have to raise the fee you are paying for this treatment from I£3,000 to I£6,000. Come, let's forget it."

I spat out the little springy instrument, got up and whispered the national slogan into the dentist's ear: "Listen, did I ask you for a receipt?"

"No, you are on the ball," the dentist agreed, "but I don't want any trouble. I declare all my income. It's a question of honor with me."

"So the hole in my tooth will have to stay?"

"No, you can pay I£48 net direct to my wife's driving teacher. If you do that we'll both be covered."

"Just a second," I thought out loud. "What am I going to say if the authorities discover in the driving teacher's books that I paid for your wife's lessons?"

"Tell them she's your lover?"

"May I see her photo?"

"I meant for taxation purposes only."

I asked him whether we could go on with the drilling, and we made a date for the end of the week. But then I ran into complications with the driving teacher. Seems he too is up to his ears in the maximum.

"Sorry," the man informed me. "Until the end of August, I won't touch money, because each additional penny puts me in a higher tax bracket. Money is out of the question."

"So couldn't I pay your grocery bill?"

"It's already been paid by the furniture manufacturer, who is learning to drive his private car. I am quite well organized," the teacher added. "The house painter who studies the motorcycle with me, for instance, the other day painted my sister's apartment in lieu of a fee. My garage bill is jointly paid by two fashion designers. Can you sing?"

"Not really."

"That's a pity. I'd like to develop my voice. Do you have a stamp collection?"

"Only key holders."

"That's junk. But you know what? Pay our babysitter in exchange for the driving lessons of your dentist's wife."

I got along nicely with the babysitter. Though at first she was afraid of negotiating with me, saying she doesn't accept money from strangers, I proposed bringing recommendations from our plumber, locksmith, seamstress, barber, gardener, electrician, beautician, general practitioner, lawyer and night watchman, all of whom can testify that I pay everything only in cash, without receipts, very discreetly and urbanely.

"No, I don't want to be in anybody's power," the babysitter persisted. "Is your tooth hurting badly?"

"It's getting worse all the time."

"Then buy me contact lenses."

"Willingly," I agreed. "But what am I going to say if they discover it in the optician's books?"

"Tell them I am your mistress."

"Sorry, but that job is taken," I informed the babysitter. "The dentist's wife already registered with me. Do you have a raincoat?"

"Yes, the young couple upstairs with the newborn baby bought me one," said the babysitter. "I am willing to settle for a weekend in Tiberias with half board."

That sounded reasonable. Later on I learned that the contact lenses too would have worked, because lately several Tel Aviv opticians started selling office supplies as well. In these maximum shops the little taxpayer buys himself spectacles and gets an official receipt for office supplies which are tax-deductible. There are also new shops selling *objets d'art* and China statuettes linked to typewriters, and somewhere in the north of Tel Aviv there is a massage parlor where they give you receipts for typing and mimeographing work. Our Mediterranean people are quick to adapt themselves to the facts of life. Nor did I run into any particular maximum difficulties at the Tiberias hotel.

"I have a room over the weekend for the driving teacher's babysitter," the boss said. "But not by telephone."

I drove down to Tiberias and discussed the matter privately, in an open field.

"All right, let's see." The boss leafed through a secret little notebook. "The first floor is taken by my son's music teacher. Next to him lives the owner of the laundry and in the royal suite my income-tax adviser. Here everything is paid for in services and merchandise. It's not worth while taking money, because eighty percent—"

"I know, I know," I agreed. "But how am I going to pay you? Could I do some dishwashing?"

"There is no vacancy," said the hotel owner. "On the other hand I have an idea: Pay my dentist."

And thus the circle closed. The hotel owner's dentist refused to accept money, because he too is in the bracket, and asked for an air ticket to Uruguay for his mother-in-law, or 3,000 eggs and 10 kilos of salt. By then I was a little tired of the maximum pursuit and decided to resign myself to the toothache until I could locate through newspaper ads a bad dentist with low maximum tax.

Anyway, the government's wise fiscal policy deserves unreserved praise for not only preventing bank liquidity but also for succeeding—for the first time in modern history—in eradicating that ancient curse of mankind and removing the evil of money as a means of payment. We have returned to the barter system of the primitive peoples, a most praiseworthy development. Before long we shall return to the trees of the governmental jungle.

🌿 *It appears that our economy is advancing with unprecedentedly large strides. While other countries of our comic size need a consolidation process extending over a dozen years in order to reach the top, the peak of economic prosperity, we, notwithstanding our crippling war expenses, find ourselves after just a few years already on the way down toward economic stagnation. But whoever thinks this is a terrible tragedy apparently cannot stand on his head. In other words, without that skill it is a little hard to find your financial legs in our country.*

A Young Person's Guide
to Financial Independence

It is no longer a secret that the possibilities for earning easy money are becoming ever more restricted. The stringent security measures taken all over our country have cut down the frequency of diamond robberies to not more than one a week, and even here there is a waiting list to the end of the next fiscal year. So the only feasible short cut to a consolidation of the individual's economic situation is bankruptcy.

Preparations

Naturally, not everyone can go bankrupt at the drop of a hat. The act demands careful preparation and great astuteness in the moment of truth. The first step in launching a bankruptcy is the establishment of a company with a ringing foreign name. The company may deal in imports, show business or haberdashery; it makes no difference as long as it is of limited liability, hereinafter "Ltd." "Liability" means that somebody is liable, while "limited" hints at the fact that it is not us. Personally, we only manage the company on its way to the scheduled bankruptcy. We sign contracts, take advances, order merchandise all over the world, request subsidies and are indefatigable. In return for these managerial services we allocate ourselves large salaries, fat bonuses, lavish expense accounts and business trips to the Bahamas. The wife also is employed with the company as deputy-bankrupt and purchases the company car for I£2.40 in easy installments.

However, people are not that gullible. Before they grant credits to a Ltd., they check whether the company has any money in the bank. It has! How come? Simple: We loan our Ltd. a certain sum of money out of our own pockets and put it in the bank where everybody can see it.

Then we go bankrupt.

This, as a matter of fact, is inevitable. Because of our huge overdrafts, the company loses its pants, and one somber day the creditors of the Ltd. meet and start playing cards with the company's bounced checks. Then there follow six rather difficult months for the little bankrupt, chockfull of threats, telephone calls, broken windowpanes and last warnings by nervous lawyers.

This period has to be borne patiently.

The Turning Point

Some time before the turning point we go to the bank and withdraw back into our pockets the loan we had advanced the company. Down to the last penny. Then we convene our creditors for a national convention in the Philharmonic Auditorium and address them in the following terms:

"Friends, I have gone bankrupt! I fought hard, I made sacrifices, I tried, but they broke me. This is a lousy country, taxes, terrific taxes. It's altogether impossible to make a living. My company hasn't got a penny to its name, only debts. This is the end. Now that I've told you the truth I feel better. Thanks for your attention."

The creditors sit all around us in the spacious concert hall and their eyes are as glassy as a masterpiece by Benvenuto Cellini, the illustrious son of Florence. They know they cannot do a thing, because it is not we who owe them money but fate—that is, the Ltd.—and after all, what can you expect from three letters? Deepest despondency reigns within the hall.

"However," we suddenly say, "however, dear friends, if you'll let me continue, if you'll give me a little breathing space, say for a month or two years, then maybe, one of these days, who knows but I may repay all the company's debts down to the last penny."

The creditors say, "Will you excuse us?" and go into a huddle in the restaurant around the corner. It doesn't take them long to realize that they have no choice. If they allow the Ltd. to declare itself officially bankrupt, they won't ever see a penny of their money, because its remaining assets will be siphoned off by the multitude of official receivers, while the bankrupt, his property safely restored, will be free as a bird, looking for new adventures. Besides, it is most unpleasant to write down in the books: "This investment turned into shit." Banks are especially reluctant to have to explain to the Comptroller checking their balance sheets: "Well, yes, this money is written off." And just between ourselves, what is there to lose? As long as the debt exists, there is at least a glimmer of hope.

The creditors' reply is therefore, "O.K., carry on!"

Here we crawl out from under the table, purple in the face.

"Carry on?" we shout in a towering rage. "Perhaps you can tell me how. How, damn it, can you ask a man to take upon himself the management of a ruined company whose safe is completely empty? You are ridiculous, so help me!"

There and then the hat is passed around and the result is I£400 in cash and I£3,600 in promissory notes.

The Pampering

In the nature of things, the Hebrew creditor is fated to chase his money till his last breath. The Ltd. manager is therefore extended new credit on condition that he does not declare himself an official bankrupt and instead continues his duties as head of the company. Then starts a marvelous period of pampering and pleasantness. It is almost incredible what one can squeeze out of an Israeli creditor whose back is to the wall. It is related that Avital Sulzbaum, the king of bankrupts, last winter made his creditors at the bankruptcy meeting drop to their knees and worship him before he graciously agreed to continue in office.

"Good Lord," the hosts of creditors prayed, "please, please keep him in good health!"

Anxious souls have been known to send their family doctor to the bankrupt, naturally at their own expense. They see to it that his sex life is well regulated, provide masseurs, etc. They slip him pocket money as well as subscription tickets to the Philharmonic. In short, they keep him swaddled in cotton wool. The creditors organize in a "Sulzbaum Club" whose registered aim is to safeguard the bankrupt manager's work capacity. It is a wonderful feeling to know that one is beloved and cherished. It is said that frequently the principal creditor has his daughter marry the bankrupt in order to insure his money. Or else he names him his legal heir. As a rule, creditors also provide a guard of honor wherever he goes.

This is a very cozy situation, this popularity, this *dolce vita*. And the moment discipline slackens or snide remarks are dropped, it is enough to raise your voice a few notches.

"As a matter of fact, what do I need this for? I'll declare myself bankrupt and be done with it!"

The collection is resumed right away, unreserved homage paid. They have no choice: We are in a position of strength because we are bankrupt.

The Danger

It sometimes happens that the bankrupt loses control over his life's work and under the influence of alcohol or in a fit of momentary recklessness starts repaying the company debts to the creditors. As long as payment is in the order of $200 a year, there is nothing to be afraid of; on the contrary, this keeps up the tension. But should he foolishly repay the whole debt, he is lost. It is well nigh impossible to describe the seething fury of the Mediterranean creditor who has received all his money back. We know of a sad case where one of the Ltd.'s government grants was, through a clerical error, transferred to a principal creditor. The man pocketed the money and then went and beat up the bankrupt.

A manager who pays up exposes himself to attack like a turtle which rashly crawls out of its shell. His fate is the fate of the ordinary honest person; all he gets is kicks and abuse. Therefore it is vital to maintain a preventive debt to the end of his days, as this is the key to a comfortable and carefree existence in the Seventies.

The Crucial Question

Readers might be tempted to ask themselves the following question: Since this sounds so easy, why doesn't everybody go bankrupt?

Who says they don't?

🌺 *The population explosion has bypassed our little country. What's more, for technical reasons beyond our control, we always had more explosions than population. Overcrowding becomes critical only during Football Cup games and military parades. The difference between the two mass events is that while for those decisive football matches the Municipality provides a huge stadium, it crowds the tens of thousands of spectators watching the parade into our apartment.*

The Great Balcony Scene

After ten days of superhuman effort Army sappers and fire-brigade volunteers succeeded in extricating from the debris Mr. Abraham Ten-Petek, former third-floor dweller of the house which had collapsed in the main street of Tel Aviv.

No sooner was Ten-Petek brought out than he asked, "Has the parade passed yet?"

The following is Ten-Petek's testimony before the ministerial investigating committee.

It all started on Independence Day dawn. The phone made me jump from my bed at 5:00 A.M.

"Hi, Yoske," a male voice boomed, "haven't seen you in years!"

"Thanks," I yawned. "And how are you?"

"So-so. You know, old boy, it's a shame that we never meet nowadays, Yoske."

"You're right," I agreed. "Though my name is Abraham. As a matter of fact, where did I have the pleasure?"

"What's the matter with you? Why, this is Misha! Don't you remember? I went to the Technion with your brother."

Gradually we warmed to each other. Misha promised to drop in for a chat at 10:30. I told my wife to prepare some snacks; my brother's childhood pal was coming. Whereupon she said she never knew I had a brother. I was rather puzzled. Especially when at 6:00 A.M. there was an unexpected ring and there on the doorstep stood the Bialazurkevitzes from Beersheba. They had brought along their children's playmates as well and their maid. The maid also had a child.

"We've been planning to pay you a visit for ages, but something always happens. Today we finally made it."

The Bialazurkevitzes protested that they didn't want to cause us any inconvenience. They'd just take a breath of fresh air on the balcony. Whereupon they quickly dispersed and dug in along the railing.

By eight o'clock, 128 of my former schoolmates had rung up to inquire about my health. Gradually it dawned on us why the Greenspans from below had disappeared two days ago, leaving on their door two huge padlocks and a sign reading "Beware! Leprosy!"

At 8:30 we disconnected the phone. Soon afterward a young man showed up with a very warm letter from Mrs. Pomerantz, in which she requested us for her sake to let her cousin watch the parade from our place. It was the first time anyone had ever approached us in such a manner. It was a great honor, even though I had never met Mrs. Pomerantz.

Then we decided not to admit any more people into our apartment. Misha could come, because of my brother, but after him we'd draw the line. We'd make an exception for our relatives; that went without saying. And we could not very well turn away the grocer with the twins. But I firmly told the milkman that he could definitely not bring any relatives apart from his parents.

By that time there was no more room on the balcony, so they pulled tables up to the window. There was a ring from the telephone company.

"Something wrong with your phone, sir?"

"No, I only disconnected it for today."

"All the same, I have to check it. Please see to it that someone is at home at ten-thirty."

I begged our family doctor not to drag the heavy clothes closet onto the balcony, but he assured me that there really wasn't anything to it; it was quite light. At ten o'clock the door was broken down and my son's schoolmates stormed in. Some of them clambered up the bookshelves; the rest placed footstools atop the piano. I berated my son for bringing the whole school home. The child protested that he did not know them at all; besides, he was only eight while the intruders were over twenty.

The situation on the balcony became critical when Misha placed a ladder on the Bialazurkevitzes' backs. A loud quarrel ensued and the brother of the maid's husband fell down onto the Greenspans' balcony. Fortunately he did not hurt himself because the balcony was packed with leprosy patients. Hearing the uproar, the district policeman came up with his little girl.

Somewhat later there arrived an elderly lady, Mrs. Pomerantz, looking for her cousin, the Yemenite dance troupe, the hairdresser, a certain Yoel Finkelstein, the Swedish minister, Judy, a gentleman from the Reparations Commission, the Titans acrobatic trio, my sister, an after-burner technician, the Brothers Karamazov and the Second Parachute brigade.

Meanwhile my guests got hungry, so I dashed down and bought five hundred bagels. Several passers-by asked whether they could come up, but I let in only a few. Afterward the Municipal Engineer arrived and warned us that it was dangerous to stay in the apartment. He asked permission for his wife to stay.

Then came Styx, whom we had called in the fall of 1952 to fix our kitchen tap, and now he had come.

At first the right wing of the balcony collapsed, so they all shifted to the left. Then the floor started sagging, so they all piled into the kitchen, from where one could also see the parade. Then it happened. The luckier among them were not completely covered by the debris, so that they could watch the march-past through the cracks in the masonry. But I missed the event.

❧ As this book goes to press the People's Republic of China reportedly has 800 million inhabitants. By 1980 they will be two-thirds of mankind, by 1990 four-fifths and in 2000 all of mankind. They have at present about 100 million soldiers. If all of this armed crowd should file past the leader's saluting base on Chinese Independence Day the march-past would last a whole year—that is, as soon as this year's parade was over they would have to start a new one, endlessly, eternally. Awful. One really could not do that to Chairman ("May a thousand flowers bloom") Mao. Sitting in the middle of the grandstand, all that time remembering his own quotes, he would be moved to tears by them.

Little Red Riding Book

Now that the Great Chinese Revolution has earned the approval of Richard Nixon, we should like, Comrades, to send warm greetings and best wishes to Chairman Mao, the world's last Marxist. And if the reader thinks that we are pulling his leg, let him take note that for some time now we have owned the book whose circulation equals that of the Bible and *Tarzan of the Apes* taken together, the red booklet which changed the face of Brezhnev: the quotations of Mao Tse-tung.

How this best seller, printed at the People's Press in Peking, came into our possession, how it was smuggled into our house from distant lands, is another story, which we have neither the time nor the space to tell here. Anyway, it is bound in people's red plastic, with the star in the center, in a very handy pocketbook form.

On page two, under a protective sheet of people's rice paper, we find Chairman Mao's likeness, an impish smile on his face as he acknowledges at the Eighth Congress of the Communist Party the spontaneous ovation which lasted for forty uninterrupted minutes in response to the Chairman's announcement: "Modesty helps one to go forward" (page 237).

And that is just one quotation out of a thousand: Vice-Chairman Lin Piao, who was honored with the task of writing a foreword to the most-waved book in the history of mankind, even laid down guidelines on the day-to-day uses of the book. "In studying the works of Chairman Mao," wrote Comrade Lin Piao, before he tried to assassinate Chairman Mao in September 1971 and was liquidated, "one should have specific problems in mind, study and apply his works in a creative way, combine study with application, first study what must be urgently applied so as to get quick results, and strive hard to apply what one is studying."

Personally, we have been acting for a long time according to the instructions for use of the late Lin Piao, and ever since life has become more pleasant in our home. If we have a problem or are seized by black despair, we simply grab the book, run through it until we come to a quote relevant to our situation, and then put the quote into practice and act accordingly.

Mao!

A few weeks ago, for instance, the little woman plumped down in front of the TV set in the living room, and in the meantime our dinner burned to a crisp, black mass on the kitchen stove. The wife was very upset and hunger gnawed at our innards, and everything seemed lost, until we took the book in hand and found the solution at the top of page 267, taken straight out of "On the People's Democratic Dictatorship," June 30, 1949, Vol. IV.

"It is hard to avoid mistakes, but we should make as few as possible," says Chairman Mao and adds: "Once a mistake is made, we should correct it, and the more quickly and thoroughly, the better."

The Chairman's deep philosophical thoughts restored youthful vigor to our exhausted limbs, and we rolled the TV set into the kitchen. Ever since, there are no cinders, no hunger, only Mao. There is no limit to the practical uses of the quotations. I won't ever forget, for instance, that fateful night when we played poker with the Seligs and I had lost a fortune and was completely wiped out, when literally on the verge of bankruptcy salvation flashed through my mind: "The Chairman!" With my remaining strength I crawled to my bed and took out the red booklet from under the pillow, ran through it a few times and found the saying which fit my situation on page 182, among the Chairman's Selected Works, June 11, 1954, Vol. III: "Be resolute, fear no sacrifice and surmount every difficulty to win victory."

In short, I returned to the game, staked I£15 on a stupid pair of kings and in the end not only recouped my money from the Seligs but got up richer by about three pounds. What matters is that the book should always be within reach. With me, unless it's in my bed, I carry it in my hip pocket or in the car's glove compartment. The wife borrows it whenever she goes out to see about municipal taxes or plays the piano. ("In playing the piano, all ten fingers are in motion; it won't do to move some fingers only and not others. But if all ten fingers press down at once, there is no melody. To produce good music, the ten fingers should move rhythmically and in coordination." Methods of Work of Party

Committees (March 13, 1949, Vol. IV, page 110).

Small wonder then that we don't part from the little red book even for a minute. Why take risks? Sometimes it is really eerie with what ease the yellow giant's quotes can be put to practical use in minor family crises. Thus, it is our daughter Ranana's delightful habit to drop everything on the floor and then cry because she has dropped them. One day of excessive droppings the wife took the book, sat down next to the baby's crib and read to her daughter the original text out of Selected Works, Vol. IV, page 3:

"Grasp firmly. That is to say, the Party committee must not merely 'grasp' but must 'grasp firmly' its main tasks. One can get a grip on something only when it is grasped firmly, without the slightest slackening. Not to grasp firmly is not to grasp at all. Naturally, one cannot get a grip on something with an open hand. When the hand is clenched as if grasping something, but is not clenched tightly, there is still no grip."

And what do you know? Our little one listened to Chairman Mao's appropriate quote and fell asleep and didn't drop another thing until she woke up.

Mao adores youth. ("Young people have to study and work. Full attention must be therefore paid to their work and studies." From a talk at the reception for the Presidium of the Second National Congress of the Youth League, June 30, 1953.) And as for war, there is a great deal to be learned from the old man in this vital field as well. Our staff officers could do worse than take to heart the "Manifesto of the Chinese People's Liberation Army," October 1947, page 167: "All officers and fighters of our army must improve their military art, march forward courageously toward certain victory in the war."

And if the reader thinks we are not quoting from

Mao's quotes, he is simply mistaken and in need of a good dose of self-criticism. Kindly consult the book. Whenever we are in a bad mood, some Mediterranean cloud darkens our porch, or anxiety slips into our heart, all we have to do is grasp (firmly) the red booklet and read a few infantile passages, penned by the Immortal Revolutionary. This infallibly restores our good humor.

The reader, too, would be wise to purchase for himself and his little family the red booklet. From then on his abode will tinkle with healthy laughter. Doctors recommend Chairman Mao. Three sayings between two pieces of matzoh before meals.

❧ *Chinese sympathy is as unobtainable for our imperialistic country as a slice of bread in a Chinese restaurant, but in Black Africa we make a lot of sense. To tell the truth, we enjoy our role of an industrial power among our dark brethren. We export to liberated Africa finished products and import from there raw students. The operation is very skillfully run by our Foreign Ministry. Whenever something is cooking in even the smallest African state, our envoy is there. Sometimes he gets cooked.*

A Coveted Position

"Hello, Ziegler. Please be seated."

"Thanks, Your Excellency."

"How long have you been with us at the Foreign Ministry?"

"Four months."

"Splendid. I'm happy to inform you, Ziegler, that we decided to detach you for service outside the frontiers and institutions of our country."

"Me? To serve abroad? At long last! Thank you."

"Don't thank me, Ziegler. This is but a fitting prize for the excellent work you have done over four whole months. True, several of your colleagues are before you in line, but at the last meeting your appointment went through without opposition. Even Birenbaum himself said, 'I think I have to renounce in Ziegler's favor.' "

"Mr. Birenbaum . . . renounced . . ."

"With all his heart. We'd like to confer on you the rank of First Consul."

"On me? First? Words fail me."

"That's all right, Ziegler. Our slogan is, make room for talent! You are leaving tomorrow morning."

"I? In the morning? Wonderful! May I assure you, Your Excellency, that I shall represent the state and its institutions with absolute loyalty."

"Of that I am convinced."

"As a matter of fact, where am I going?"

"To the Congo."

"Congo?"

"Congo."

"Tomorrow?"

"Yes. Why?"

"Nothing. That is, I thought we already had a consul there."

"Yes, quite possibly we might still have one. Anyway, up until yesterday we had radio contact with him. In his last message, at two-forty-five A.M., he announced, 'African soldiers are entering the building, searching for fat white men.'"

"And?"

"The transmission broke off at that point. What's the matter, Ziegler?"

"I wonder, Your Excellency, whether I may take upon myself such a highly sensitive mission. After all, there are more experienced people in the party."

"Oh, come off it, Ziegler. We all place great hopes in your strengthening relations between our country and the Dark Continent at present liberating itself from the rule of the white man."

"Your Excellency's faith in me fills me with pride. Yet, I ask myself, will my limited experience suffice to carry out my difficult mission?"

"I am convinced that you will fulfill your duty

faithfully, with discrimination and wisdom."

"In my view, Mr. Birenbaum is superior to me in all respects. I think he is superbly suited to the Congo post. As a matter of fact, who am I and what am I to cheat him out of his due?"

"Modesty is a virtue, but it is not always in place, Ziegler. The consideration of our amicable ties with the Congolese tribes is a cause very dear to all of us. Are you any good at unarmed combat?"

"Who, me?"

"Never mind, we'll give you a quickie course. Report tomorrow morning at a certain Army camp and the day after tomorrow you'll be off."

"How am I going to travel?"

"By plane, naturally. They'll drop you somewhere near Leopoldville. You'll have to walk only a few miles through the jungle in the area of the Kootchy-Mootchy tribe."

"Shouldn't you have another talk with Birenbaum?"

"Leave that coward alone. You, Ziegler, I am certain, can run as fast as a hare, are an excellent swimmer and can climb trees. You are our man."

"I don't speak Belgian."

"It won't be necessary. All you need is a pleasant personality and diplomatic skill. Should you meet tribal warriors on the road, all you have to do is raise your hands and shout, 'Israel! Golda!' The chieftain will immediately mellow, grin, embrace you and signal to his warriors to drop the poisoned arrows and clubs."

"And if the chieftain does not mellow and grin, what do I do then?"

"Intone the Hatikvah."

"I've got no singing voice."

"It doesn't matter. Try to present your credentials before the aborigines have time to throw their elephant spears. You could also quickly offer three study grants. The main thing: a clever approach, refinement and tact."

"Birenbaum . . ."

"He renounced in your favor. Congratulations, Ziegler. Good luck. Drop us a line now and then."

"Your Excellency!"

"Yes?"

"Won't they eat me?"

"I'm not a prophet. In any event, I trust you to show them that you'll always remain a man of taste."

❦ The United States is the main supplier of arms for Israel, one may say the only one, especially before elections. The mutual relationship is very friendly indeed. Only a bit exhausting.

Torture Chamber, D.C.

"Be seated," President Nixon said as he shook my hand, smiling broadly. "How are things at home?"

"Thanks," I said and sat down in the armchair facing his desk. "The weather has been rather rainy lately, but still all right for flying."

"I'm pleased to hear that. I will be out fishing over the weekend."

"Indeed?"

"Yes."

Here our lively conversation ground to a stop. The President smiled cordially and pointed through the window at the White House Rose Garden.

"I think the lawn ought to be mowed. What do you think?"

"Absolutely," I said and added quickly, "we want Phantoms."

The President turned toward me, his face wreathed in smiles.

"You need those planes, don't you?"

"Yes, Mr. President."

"I am happy to inform you that I have already given your request my close attention. My decision has been taken."

"Taken?"

"Taken. Tea or coffee?"

"Yes."

"Personally, I prefer weak tea. How many spoons?"

"Thirty-five."

"I take saccharine, not that it matters, but my wife is watching my waistline. I play golf every Friday with Senator Fulbright. Why don't you join us sometime?"

"Thank you."

"It has been a pleasure meeting you. I am sure I will see you again."

Mr. Nixon shook my hand, smiling broadly.

"Mr. President," I said, "those planes are a matter of life or death for us."

"So it seems," Mr. Nixon agreed. "Therefore I won't delay my answer any longer."

"Thank you so much."

"You are welcome. That is my motto: If you have got an answer, give it right away, on the spot, without delay, without unnecessary tension. In other words, if you can't make up your mind, shut up, but if you have taken a decision like me, announce it without further ado. Every minute counts, every second. Why torture your fellow man, right?"

"Right, so—"

"That's how I always acted. I am a born quick-decision maker. By the way, this reminds me of an excellent joke. Do you know it? A Jewish voter in New Yorks says, 'My dad always voted Democrat and my granddad too, and so I will vote for them as well.' Then someone from my party, the Republican, asks him, 'And if your dad were a horse thief and your granddad too, would you also be a horse thief?' 'No,' the Jew answers, 'then I would be a Republican.' Ha-ha-ha."

"Ha."

"An excellent joke. I heard it the other day from one of the oil-company representatives."

"Did you meet them?"

"They live here. What was it that we were talking about?"

"The Phantoms."

"Yes." The President smiled cordially. "Believe me, it was not easy to reach a decision. There are all sorts of global considerations pro and con. For instance, on the one hand, you are the only true democracy in the area, but on the other, you are also the friends of the United States. True, all by yourselves you block the advance of the Russians, but the Arabs serve them faithfully. You need those arms to insure your survival, but it should not be forgotten even for a moment that you pay us cash. You certainly need those planes; on the other hand, it cannot be denied that I have publicly promised them to you. All these contradictions add up to a very delicate complication, you see. But in the end I did make up my mind. It is final, it is definite, it is beyond any doubt."

"So, Mr. President . . ."

"My decision is unequivocal and speaks for itself. Would you like to write it down?"

"I'll remember it."

"You are one hundred percent right. One has to keep one's word. An honest man stands up to be counted. If you said yes, it has got to be yes, and if you said no, it's no. If you said, we'll see, it's we'll see. If you say, it is scrambled eggs, it is scrambled eggs. It is the same with coleslaw. I could give you many more examples, but I don't want to waste any more of your precious time. Won't you drop in next week?"

"I'd prefer now. I implore you . . . Now . . ."

"I see, I see. Just a second."

Here the President stepped over to his secretary and donated 1,000 planes to South Vietnam, 60 to Iran, 100 to Saudi Arabia and 70 to People's China. Afterward Mr. Nixon had a light meal and a nap and exchanged a few words with the Marquis de Sade in Washington on an advanced training course.

"I am so sorry," the President said on returning, smiling cordially. "What can I do for you, sir?"

"The Phantoms, Mr. President, the Phantoms."

"Yes, yes, now I remember. You will get my final answer within six minutes."

With that the President took out his watch and placed it in front of him on the desk. He fixed his eyes on the dial and from time to time sent me a friendly smile.

"It's getting late, isn't it?" He broke the silence fifteen minutes later. "Would you like to see something on TV?"

"The planes, sir."

"Of course! Did I tell you that I had taken my final decision?"

"Yes, you took it."

"Believe me, I have no intention of keeping you on tenterhooks any longer."

"Thank you."

"To cut a long story short."

"Yes!"

"Openly, as among friends."

"Yes, yes, yes."

"The planes you want . . ."

"*Oy.*"

"Are, according to my best judgment . . ."

"*Oy . . .*"

"Without prejudice and without fear . . ."

"Without . . ."

"Straight from the shoulder without beating about the bush . . ."

"Without . . . without . . ."

"In short . . ."

"Yes . . ."

"How is Golda?"

Here I rose and crawled completely exhausted toward the door.

"Where are you going?" the President asked, smiling broadly. "Don't you realize that I am about to announce my favorable decision on the Phantoms?"

"Thanks," I said. "They are now obsolete."

❧ *The much vaunted El Fatah and other Arab terror movements were set up with the praiseworthy aim of eradicating the despicable Israeli imperialistic state and replacing it with a democratic, binational one, in which Arabs and Jews would live and die—in just that order. At first the eradicating progressed nicely, but the day after the movement was set up it was found that the Israelis were shooting back out of habit. It was then decided to switch to the blowing up of civilian airliners in Europe. This was not exactly identical with the original aim; still it was better than nothing at all.*

The Outcasts

The place: Munich airport. The time: 1971, A.M. We are returning home from culture-soaked Europe by a plane not of our national airline.

"Are these your suitcases?" the blond clerk asks while checking our upside-down Israeli passports. "Didn't anyone ask you to take a parcel along?"

"No, we assure you, no one." As a matter of fact, we had read only two days ago about the marvelous farce at Athens airport. It all looks so simple: You simply walk into the cockpit and announce, "Hello, I've got a hand grenade in my pocket. Put me through to the President of the state. Hi, hand over the murderers, the Fort Knox treasury and shish-kebab for two. I repeat, I've got a hand grenade in my pocket."

We take a look around. The flight is fully booked. In the queue to the blond clerk a young hippie with a black mustache and suspicious sunglasses is pushing and shoving. Is he our broadcaster? Our eyes also roam the place in search of the counterpoint. "Who is our air marshal?" the Israeli passengers ask, but the little woman says no, only El Al dispenses that comfort.

Our plane is not listed on the illuminated flight schedule until the very last moment. Naturally, we are moved to the farthest corner of the departure lobby, to the Troubles Department. Before long, German police arrive armed with submachine guns and survey us with basilisk eyes. All around, people move away from us and watch the refugees with quiet and subdued scorn. As for ourselves, we shrink to the limits of credibility. After all, it is rather unpleasant that alone among the world's peoples we should be the eternal troublemakers. The French fly quietly, the Poles fly quietly, the Arabs fly quietly; only the Jews turn all airports topsy-turvy. An arrogant, aggressive race, to quote someone.

At the entrance to a cramped solitary-confinement cell at the end of the hall, a police sergeant addresses us: "Go along in couples and take all your luggage with you."

Behind the door, a close cross-examination is taking place. Every couple carries out a private identification parade among its suitcases and submits for inspection even its embarrassingly empty purses. The detectives plunge their arms right to their shoulders into the luggage and sometimes emerge with soiled stockings clinging to their fingers. All metal objects are scrutinized, every box is cautiously opened. The team does not openly blame us for this tomfoolery, but their icy stares are eloquent: "Gypsies, that's what you are." The Wandering Jew goes home. Standing there, wedged in by the growing mountains of our upended belongings, with the kids' toys in one hand and a bunch of keys in the other, we are gripped by the mute fear that next thing we know we'll be arrested and moved to the central prison for some advanced grilling. Who will stand us bail?

"Stop!" a plainclothesman barks behind us. "What's that in your hand, sir?"

"A camera."

He releases me. The wife is fighting the sergeant and the suitcase locks. It all takes ages. From the outside dozens of impatient passengers are pounding on the door. Noise, nerves, shouting—in short: Israelis.

Our glance sweeps toward the center of the plush lobby. Near the exit to the Arab Airline plane, cultured gentlemen and their ladies are sitting or walking in comfort. They enjoy their cigars, chat pleasantly; they haven't got a worry in the world because they are citizens of civilized countries in the Mediterranean area, countries which give no trouble to airport managers. They are a living proof that even a nation fighting a war can maintain its dignity. In Munich, the Arabs represent Europe and we the darkest Levant. They can even send home parcels, while for us a ban is in force with no end in sight. Everybody knows that those Israelis are always causing trouble.

We take a few steps toward the group waiting for the Cairo flight to be called. It is literally touching how bucolically things are managed there, to what extent our neighbors trust us regarding international travel arrangements. The Arabs know they can have full confidence in us, that we shall never lower ourselves to their level, that we are gentlemen. Their trust pays off: They roam the world as gentlemen, while we are harassed like a flock of gypsies beset by a posse of vigilantes.

As a matter of fact, why haven't we got a terror

group of our own?

Why must we be the only ones who keep asking: How long will this go on? Why haven't we got a national movement equipped with hand grenades, Kalatchnikov guns and recoilless rifles, whom the authorities cannot curb? "This is the Jewish Democratic Front for the Liberation of Samaria and Judea. We have taken command of the plane. Over."

A dream, so help us.

An armored bus ferries us culprits to the isolated plane pasturing at the deserted edge of the field. Three jeeploads of armed cops travel along. In the succinct words of our master and mentor, the head of the Palestine Liberation Movement: The blowing up of a Jewish plane abroad is more effective publicity-wise than a massacre in Jerusalem. Our master and mentor is right. We climb the gangway in a somber mood.

At the other end of the airfield the proud eagle of the United Arab Republic takes off elegantly. He flies majestically and safely into the sun, a gentlemanly plane. Many runways away, concealed from the human eye, a planeload of outcasts slinks off.

🌷 *From time to time our friends succeed in hijacking a plane carrying Israeli passengers and land it in one of the proverbially hospitable neighboring countries. Then, within the framework of the international law, they demand the exchange of hostages for the terrorists held by us. In May 1972, with this in mind, they landed a Sabena plane right in the heart of Israel, at Lod airport. It was a grievous mistake, on their part, to give us the home-team advantage. Ever since the Lod incident the Geneva Red Cross has been cross with us because we managed to rescue the plane passengers from being blown up, without the assistance of their organization, by unfair cunning—one might even say illegally.*

Hansel and Gretel:
A Grim Fairy Tale

It was quite an ordinary morning at the house of the wicked witch. Hansel was locked up in a cage waiting for the witch to eat him up, while poor Gretel was forced to drag in dry twigs from the woods to heat up the oven, in expectation of her brother's frying. She was crying bitterly while making these preparations. It will be remembered that ever since their mother had left them in the middle of the forest, communications between Hansel and Gretel and their parents had broken down, and they had blundered into the courtyard of the witch's house, which was made of gingerbread.

"Hurry up, stupid," the wicked witch snarled at Gretel. "Today I'm going to eat your brother, and then you as well, I hope."

"Yes, ma'am," Gretel replied. "I'm almost ready."

Just then a distinguished gentleman entered the house. His every feature reflected noble humanitarian feelings and a deep love of mankind.

"I'm Dr. Fromage, representative of the International Red Cross," he introduced himself. "I was sent here to offer my good offices."

You can imagine how great was the joy of the poor children. "Help us!" Hansel cried, "save us, good sir, because this witch plans to eat me at her earliest convenience." But Dr. Fromage immediately set things in their proper perspective.

"No, no, I don't intend to intervene in local quarrels," he said. "It is my duty to guard the lives and safety of all children and witches, wherever they may be." And he shook the hands of the landlady and her dinner with the same cordiality and even apologized to the witch for Hansel's immoderate outburst, thus succeeding in restoring the witch's confidence in the International Red Cross.

"Say," the witch mused, "this man is indeed remarkably neutral."

Then the half-blind monster ordered Hansel to stick a finger through the bars of the cage so that she might touch it and check whether or not he had been satisfactorily fattened up. The smart kid put out a dried chicken bone, as he did every morning, to show her that he was still skinny.

"Damn it," the witch fumed, "what a dry finger you have, stupid."

"I beg your pardon," Dr. Fromage intervened, "this is not at all a finger, but only a dry bone." And he upbraided Hansel and Gretel for their ruse, because, he said, as official representative of the Red Cross, he could not condone any deceitful acts. This would constitute cooperation with one of the parties to the dispute.

"You know, I am beginning to love the Geneva Convention," the witch exclaimed, and immediately decided to fry Hansel in the oven, and went out to fetch various spices. The children grabbed their unexpected chance and implored Dr. Fromage:

"Uncle," cried Gretel, shedding bitter tears, "if you have a heart, please open my poor brother's cage and set him free."

"I could do that only with the written consent of the witch," the gentleman said with a sad smile, adding in a whisper: "I must ask you to show understanding for my position. Should the witch find that I am helping you to avoid the frying, no witch on earth will ever again cooperate with the representatives of our organization, and we should not be able to work in future with maximum efficiency towards reducing the general suffering of mankind."

"That is certainly a lofty aim," Hansel shouted from his cage, "but should the Red Cross cease to work, it seems to me that the witches as well will suffer."

"No, they won't," Dr. Fromage promptly retorted, "because they are eating children, but the children are not eating witches. Therefore it is a primary duty of our international organization to establish firm relations with the community of witches, and not with the children who are being eaten up."

The children realized that their fate was sealed and they burst into loud sobs. "Woe to us," they sighed, "really woe to us."

"Now is the time to mediate," Dr. Fromage decided, producing a white flag from under his coat and starting to wave it vigorously. He went out to the witch and reported to her faithfully. "The children are saying, 'woe to us, really woe to us.' "

"Oh, that's very nice," the witch said while she gathered the spices in her apron. "The tears will give the silly fools a pleasantly salty taste."

Dr. Fromage returned with his flag to the children and continued the negotiations.

"The witch has requested me to inform you," he reported, "that the tears will give you, silly fools, a pleasantly salty taste, over."

With that he contacted the Geneva headquarters and requested precise guidelines. But it was found that in all of the Charter there was not a single paragraph worthy of that name for dealing with the barbecuing of children and their organized consumption, and therefore there was no possibility for further initiative.

In the meantime certain events had happened in the witch's lair. The wicked witch showed Gretel how she could easily shove her brother in the oven, and she demonstrated what she had in mind by bending down in front of the oven mouth, whereupon the clever girl quickly pushed the witch in and banged the iron door shut on her. You can imagine Hansel and Gretel's joy at their miraculous rescue; but just then the humanitarian messenger rushed in and, lightning-quick, released the witch from the fiery oven, apologizing for the act of violence perpetrated on her with unfair cunning.

"As long as I am in the area," Dr. Fromage said, "the status quo in this house will not be changed by force."

"Right you are," replied Hansel who had got out of the cage all by himself, and he smashed the witch's broom on Dr. Fromage's head, and even kicked his ass. Then the children, freed of their complexes, made a big fire in the oven, fried the witch to a crisp and ate her, singing patriotic songs. And they had never before eaten anybody as tasty.

🌷 *And now the closing chapter of a brief war novel dealing with the exploits of El Fatah, who extended their operations from the airports of Europe to Amman, the capital of Jordan, until King Hussein came down on them with all the armored cars at his disposal in the spirit of Arab brotherhood and scattered them to the four corners of the world. However, a substantial segment of the terrorists scattered into one corner only, toward Israel, the sole haven of understanding and humane treatment, and surrendered in their serried ranks to the Israeli defense forces. This surprised only the editors of the world's weekly magazines. In our eyes nothing could have been more logical.*

Love Story

The warrior spent the night in a tree. During the day he and another terrorist had crawled past the king's half-tracks, till at last they had reached the border of their dreams. They lit a fire and were just roasting a rabbit over it when the pursuers appeared on a hill.

"Arabs!" his friend whispered to him. "Come on, Factor, let's hide!"

They had called him "Factor" in the movement ever since the sensational interview he had granted a *Time* magazine reporter about a year before, as a result of which his picture had appeared on the cover with the caption: "The Indispensable Factor in Any Peace Settlement." Now the Factor put out the fire and the two of them scrambled up a tree with the rabbit. Secure at the top, they cast a yearning glance at the green line on the horizon, beyond which a warm press and a secure job awaited them. Factor had decided to become a milkman, whereas his friend was rather inclined to opt for a job as watchman, or to keep a kiosk. They swore softly at Yasser Arafat, that imbecile with his sunglasses, who had almost shattered their dreams with his crackpot notions.

"Listen, Factor," the other terrorist confessed in a whisper, "maybe Zionism was an historical error once, but today it sure comes in handy."

But the Factor had fallen asleep, and in his dream was again playing backgammon with Moshe Dayan or strolling arm in arm through the Valley. In the morning he sustained a medium injury. He had suddenly remembered the Israeli publicists of the Progressive Camp and Prophetic Vision, and in a fit of laughter had fallen out of the tree and twisted his left ankle. His friend bandaged it, said "Sorry, mate," and disappeared west. Alone Factor limped on toward freedom. Several times that day he was spotted by the king's soldiers, who opened mortar fire on him, but he managed to hide between the rocks.

At dusk he crossed the Yarmuk River, his heart filled with apprehension. A single nightmare had been haunting him all along: He reaches the Promised Land at long last, and there is no trace of any Israeli soldiers, leaving him there lost and forlorn, a lone orphan in a reporterless field. Factor stripped off his undershirt and waved it at the planes passing indifferently overhead, then threw himself down and beat his fists against the cruel earth.

"Border Police," he wailed, "where are you, Border Polee-hee-eece!"

He was incredibly homesick. A tiny white cloud

appeared down below, traveling along the highway. The Factor slipped down the hillside whooping. But the command car was receding fast and the terrorist gave chase.

"Wait!" he yelled and fired his Kalatchnikov in the air. "Comrades, wait for me! I'm a terrorist! El Fatah! *Time* magazine! You can't leave me like this!"

The command car stopped, a company sergeant-major got out and waited for the Factor to come up to him. The terrorist's heart overflowed, and with a muffled sob he fell upon the CSM's neck, then blew his nose into the handkerchief given him. Later, in the moving car, he calmed down, leaned back in his seat and just smiled to himself. He felt a fierce love for these people, had always felt himself one of them. After all these years as a wandering Factor, now for the first time he felt peaceful and secure, among his brethren.

"By Allah," he said, snuggling up against the CSM, "east is east and west is west, but there's no place like home."

🦋 *Now here is somebody who is still alive, though only by chance: Hassan the Second, King of Morocco. The reader may remember that the latest attempt on his life again failed through technical shortcomings in the execution, though the circumstances were, to say the least, foggy. When writing future history books, scholars will have quite a job sorting out the wealth of material and controlling their fits of laughter.*

The Rabat Hunt

What appears beyond all doubt is the fact that thirty army trucks filled with the flower of the military college managed to infiltrate the birthday party of Hassan the Second without attracting any attention. The cadets had been told by their officers that they were going to rescue the King from soldiers brought by army trucks in order to kill him, but all signs indicate that the cadets changed their minds on the way and decided among themselves to kill the King too, except that their commanders, who were plotting to kill Hassan, didn't know that; hence the regrettable lack of coordination.

When the flower of the military college broke into the garden of the Summer Palace and opened fire on the guests, everyone thought they were watching a pageant with male chorus and applauded warmly, to be most disappointed when they found they were dead. The King himself rushed at the revolters with open arms, whereupon the 130 outstanding cadets began discharging lethal volleys of machine gun, bazooka, Katyusha and cannon fire at the King, narrowly missing him so that only two diplomats and one insurance agent at the other end of the garden were killed.

The confusion was considerable. Someone shouted, "Put out the lights!" but that proved impossible since it was two in the afternoon. The college flowers fired some more and mowed down a lot of their officers, who were frantically searching for the King. Apparently, while preparing for the revolt they had forgotten what Hassan looked like and were now obliged to move from man to man and from corpse to corpse to inquire of each whether he wasn't by any chance king or something.

Hassan himself was duly asked as well, but replied in the negative: "No," he said, "We are not the King."

One vigilant cadet pointed to the crown on his head. "And that," he asked, "what's that?"

"That's nothing," said Hassan. "I'm a hippie."

Thus, miraculously, the King was saved. What is more, he volunteered to lead the rebels through the Summer Palace for a guided room-to-room search, while at the same time the officers of the revolution announced over the loudspeakers, "Will Hassan the Second please come down to Information right away!" They repeated the announcement in every language, but only a German banker by the name of Koenig showed up and was shot out of hand. The situation was rather awkward really. Here they were at the palace at last, all ready to give history a new turn, and nobody remembered what the King looked like. Only one second lieutenant had a picture in his pocket, but that turned out to be President Nixon, who was in Washington just then, rather out of range. Someone else recalled that the King was short and usually dressed in a general's uniform, with the result that most high officers under 1.65 meters tall were finished off with grenades.

Meanwhile, another bunch of flowers had seized the radio station and declared a republic, to be followed by a military parade the next morning. King Hassan had already gone through every wing of his spacious palace at the head of his cadets, leaping across the stiffs, the boys behind him completely done in. In the kitchen they discovered General Ahmed Medbouh, the leader of the rebels, with a headache, hunting for something to put on his throbbing temples, so they let him have it, thus felling the brilliant brain behind the revolution. To make up for that, the search was joined by the head of Security, General Oufkir, who suddenly emerged from the lavatory, and the King transferred authority to him while running two abreast.

"Catch," whispered the King to the general. "We're fed up with this whole party."

At this stage a few of the cadets began to notice that this fellow at their head kept talking about himself in the plural and voiced their misgivings that he might be Hassan. However, they recalled at once the order to kill Hassan the Second and carried on searching for the second one, the while doing some bumping-off here and there on impulse. All this running up and down stairs was beginning to tire them, however, so that in the state-room General Oufkir came to a halt and called a technical victory for Hassan. All the cadets went down on their knees and kissed the King's hand and asked for his autograph, at the same time liquidating the remaining two doctors to sum up the day's news. The King himself, appearing pleased with developments, wished them success with their careers and handed out key rings to everybody except General Oufkir, who was busy putting the country under house arrest.

The budding officers were rather muddled. "They

told us there was a party," they said apologetically, "and now they pick on us because we're Moroccans."

When the cadets discovered their officers had misled them and that in a republic, too, you have to pay taxes, they apologized and were shot through the head at once. The King went on the air and uttered some harsh criticism of the level of execution of the revolt. While these words are being written the second batch is being executed at Rabat, which goes to show how one ought to be very careful about revolutions. Before one gets going it is always advisable to find out what it is all about.

A small, aggressive state surrounded by enemies and hostile friends must from time to time take advantage of the surprise element. For instance, at the height of the present war, we appointed as Prime Minister a seventy-three-year-old grandmother and dispatched her to the world's leaders that they may argue with her. Admittedly, this was a blow below the belt, but what can you expect from a desperate nation whose back is to the wall?

Grandmother, Why Is Your Handbag So Big?

President Nixon was again awakened at dawn by his own shouts: "Rogers! . . . Rogers! . . ."

At the President's request, the Secretary of State had slept during the past few nights on the big leather couch in the Oval Room.

He hurried to the President's bedside. "It's only a dream, only a dream. She hasn't arrived yet."

Nixon breathed heavily, as if he had just been chased around the block, and his face clearly showed how overwrought he was.

"Rogers," he whispered, "don't leave me now."

The endless consultations with his aides had gone on for over a fortnight. All agreed that the President would have to prepare himself for the meeting, both with special calisthenics for strengthening the neck muscles and with extensive practice of psychological-warfare methods. The State Department secret report expressly stated that the President would now be able to withstand a reasonable barrage of remonstrances and demands, but his resistance would crumble in the emotional confrontation.

"It is to be assumed," the secret report stated, "that the Israeli Prime Minister will exploit her superior emotional status as an active grandmother."

The President was highly alert to the problem. "What am I going to do," he asked, "if she starts crying?"

"Don't look at her," Kissinger advised. "If Golda ever catches your eye you are lost. Shut your eyes at critical moments, Mr. President, and hum, mutedly, but pointedly, 'We Shall Overcome.'"

Ronald Ziegler proposed that the President should have another practice round with Mrs. Nehru. Others looked into the possibilities of hypnosis. "I'm not afraid of her. I am the President of the United States. I am not afraid!" The head of the FBI recommended the installation of a secret button under the desk. Should she start weeping, the President would surreptitiously press it and right away he would be connected by phone with Senator Fulbright.

"But I won't stay here alone," the President insisted. "Rogers has got to stay next to me all the time."

He was particularly afraid of Golda's ample black handbag.

"I am sure it is crammed with photos of missiles and grandchildren."

Since last week, about a dozen outsized handbags had been scattered all over the President's study, so that he could become accustomed to their sight. During the last few days he had already dared to touch them and even looked inside one once or twice. But his tactics were still lagging. This morning, the training exercise with Rogers had again not gone so smoothly.

Rogers cued the President from the scenario the RAND people had prepared. "Before I left, I had a talk with my little grandson. He asked me, 'Granny, are the Americans our friends?' "

"Five hundred million dollars of economic aid," Nixon muttered, "plus—"

"Not yet," Rogers interrupted the President. "Only after 'Jewish children' in the next cue. Let's go on: 'I was shocked, Mr. President, and answered my little grandson: Don't you know that Uncle Dick loves Jewish children?' Now: five hundred . . .'"

"Five hundred million dollars of economic aid, plus food surpluses."

"My grandson's eyes filled with tears. 'Granny, why doesn't Uncle Dick give us Phantoms?' "

"Fifteen years' credit and housing grants and tax-free overtime."

" 'Uncle Dick promised you to defend us, didn't he, Granny?' "

"Here she'll cry," the President broke in. "I can feel it in my fingertips that here she will cry. What shall I do?"

"You too start crying. After all, you'll soon be a grandfather yourself."

"That won't do, Rogers. She'll always be ahead of me in grandchildren." The President sighed and added bitterly, "Why am I not a woman? Why?"

The President still held the important trump, that sophisticated electronic gadget which homes in instantly on Soviet rockets and within a thousandth of a second feeds back the information that there is nothing to be done about them. In the meantime, special delaying tactics had been perfected. The clock on the wall had been moved forward five minutes, the President's servants were trained to pour the tea with excruciating slowness, and it was arranged that every fifteen minutes a new report on American casualties in Vietnam would be presented to the President. It was also agreed that when Golda got to the secret Chinese–Russian–American negotiations, the President would excuse himself for a moment and Rogers would hold the fort until his return.

"Rogers, where are you?" the President mumbled. "Don't leave me alone now."

"I'm here, Mr. President, right next to you."

The two of them looked at the clock, their faces as white as the House. 11:05. A car pulled up outside.

"Six hundred millions in cash plus a bonus for the holidays and paid vacations," the President repeated *sotto voce*.

"On second thought," Rogers croaked, "I'm dropping my plan for Israeli withdrawal."

"Too late!"

Nixon retreated slowly toward the heavy desk and with a quick movement swallowed two green pills. Steps were approaching in the lobby. The appointments secretary came in.

"Mrs. Meir has arrived."

Rogers broke into hysterical shrieks and sprinted to the back entrance, but the President had already locked it. Rogers remained glued to the wall; his legs went numb. The President leaned on the edge of his desk and breathed deeply. On the threshold there appeared the long shadow of Golda with her ample handbag.

🌿 *Whether she likes it or not, Golda leaves her personal imprint on all aspects of our life. For instance,
during her last visit to the United States, TV inquisitors
asked her whether she would request many weapons
from President Nixon and she replied with great
aplomb: "I've brought along a large shopping basket."
Whereupon the Israel Basketball Association got a
bright idea.*

The Oracle

The basketball crisis reached a new high the other
week when the coach of the national team clashed with
the Basketball Commission of the Sports Authority over
the tactics to be used in the game against the Polish
team. The committee heads advocated the "individual
interference" method, while the coach obstinately stuck
to "area interference," claiming that only this method
was effective in a game where most of the opposition
players were about 6'6", while the average of our players
was thirty-one years. Three meetings had already taken
place in an attempt to settle the dispute, and there had
also been contacts with middle-echelon government
officials, but none of the parties would budge an inch
from their positions.

"Well," they said in the end, "let's see Golda."

From the outset this had been inevitable. As a
matter of fact, this step even had some parliamentary-
administrative logic in its favor, because since sport as
such has no official standing in our country and therefore lacks a sponsor, it naturally belongs, like so many

other matters, under the umbrella of the Prime Minister's office. The meeting with Golda was arranged only
at the personal intervention of the Director-General, as
the Prime Minister had an extremely crowded schedule
that week, having to deal with the teachers' salary demands, the cost-of-living index, the postmen's strike and
Mr. Rogers. But the Prime Minister finally agreed to
the meeting, and the group filed into her office at 7:30
A.M. sharp.

First there was a brief ceremony. The chairman of
the Basketball Commission, visibly moved, greeted the
Prime Minister on behalf of Israel's basketballers and
voiced the hope that the Prime Minister would find
some way of breathing life into this important sport, as
only she, Golda, sorry, the Prime Minister . . .

Here the Prime Minister interrupted the speaker.
"All right, all right," she beamed, "but why did you pick
on me?"

The coach of the national team took the floor and
with a slight tremor in his voice explained to the Prime
Minister what the quarrel was about—i.e., that he was
for area interference, as this made effective blocking
possible in the case of technical superiority. Afterward
the head of the committee outlined to the Prime Minister the advantages of individual interference, preventing
sudden breakthroughs in the wings.

"That is the situation, madam," the chairman
summed up, "and now the decision is in your hands."

The PM surveyed the opposing camps, visibly
amused, and shook her head signifying that she did not
understand what all the fuss was about.

"I think both methods are quite acceptable," she
said. "Why can't you use both?"

It was as if an electric current had passed through

those present. Yes, this was the woman's greatness, damn it; she always found the only possible compromise, even in the most complicated situations. Really, why hadn't they thought of it before? A combination of the two methods! This was bound to lend quite a different aspect to the development of this important sport. The delegation felt greatly relieved; their faces broke into broad grins. The PM, in excellent spirits, related that she too, on her doctor's suggestion, engaged in sports: Every morning lying on her back on her bedroom rug she did gymnastics, and it was doing her a world of good.

"By the way," she asked, "what is basketball?"

"It is a struggle between two camps," her bureau chief explained. "Each camp attempts to throw and pass the ball against the other's fierce opposition, through a wide loop—'basket'—suspended from a high pole."

Then instructions were given to bring in the ornamental basket which had been prepared especially for the event. The pole with the marble plaque and the basket woven of silver thread were brought in from the lobby and the coach of the national team demonstrated some typical throws while dashing toward the basket. Clouds of dust arose in the room. The PM cleared her throat quietly and motioned with her hand, coughing, that they should stop this nonsense.

"Don't run about," she said, coughing. "Throw it without hopping around like maniacs!"

The coach stopped dead in his tracks on hearing these words. But . . . but . . . this was the basic idea of the famous "Harvard system"! Instead of throwing the ball while running toward the basket, score while standing still on the ground! The coach exchanged meaningful glances with his assistants and whispered the words which were to mold Israeli basketball in the coming decade: "As of now we throw without leaping!"

It was indeed a solemn occasion. They all felt that the brief visit, the purpose of which had been to settle a trifling misunderstanding, was now about to bear un-dreamed-of fruit.

"Shouldn't we get her to pick the boys for the selected?" the enthusiastic chairman whispered to the coach, and, at the latter's nodded assent, respectfully requested that the PM point out the players who in her view were worthy of representing our country in international meets.

"But," the PM said, "I don't even know them."

Thereupon a group photo taken in training camp was placed before her. It was a big photo in an ornamental frame prepared especially for the occasion. With maternal pride the Prime Minister's glance swept over the sturdy boys. Yes, this was a different Jewish youth, vigorous, sports-loving.

"That poor fellow," she suddenly sighed. "All are powerful, well built, only this bespectacled one is tall and skinny like a beanstalk. Why did you take him? These gangling fellows move so awkwardly."

That is how the country's best player was dropped from the national team. The delegation became a trifle worried. The coach's face clearly reflected the intense inner conflict in progress between orders from above and certain professional principles. In the end the man swallowed hard and in a whispered stutter explained to the Prime Minister something about certain scoring advantages enjoyed by players over 6'6".

"Only a true giant can actually reach the rim of the basket," he told her, "because the basket is suspended very high up."

"So you'll have to lower it," the PM decreed. "It would be unjust to discriminate against shorties."

At this point the secretary came in and announced that the Chief of Staff was waiting outside. The delegation expressed their thanks for the important rulings made during the solemn occasion and left the office overcome with emotion. Once outside, the dispute was naturally renewed. The heads of the commission interpreted the Prime Minister's directives to the effect that all the country's baskets would henceforth be lowered by at least four feet, while the coach of the national team insisted on a maximum of one foot, and even that in his opinion would be commented on adversely abroad.

The discussion degenerated into insults, the two parties parting in a new atmosphere of crisis. Seems the PM will again have to intervene in person.

❧ "No one is a prophet in his home town," the hoary old proverb affirms, hinting at the fact that it is easier for a man to succeed abroad than in his own country. Discriminating Israeli audiences have always made special efforts to disprove this libelous proverb to visiting foreign artists. "Look," they seem to be telling them, "for you this is a foreign country and yet you flop as if you were at home."

Maria Callas vs. Workers' Committee

"Have you heard the Divine?"

"Yes, I was at her concert on Wednesday. I think I am not exaggerating when I say that it was a feast for the eye as well as for the ear. Maria Callas is undoubtedly the world's greatest singer today. My hat is off to Presence Sulzbaum."

"Who's that?"

"The impresario who brought her here. Until quite recently he had been a diver on the Red Sea coast, but his brother-in-law had known Maria Callas' mother in Athens and had her signed on. A nice coup for a beginner impresario, isn't it? It was also a bright idea to rent the National Theater for the festive opening and invite our high life. The place definitely has class. I suppose you may call me quite sophisticated, but I was really thrilled when Miss Callas first appeared behind the curtain."

"Did you say 'behind the curtain'?"

"Yes, the evening started off with a slight hitch. They advertised that the concert would start at eight-thirty sharp, but there was some delay and the audience started clapping impatiently."

"Isn't it awful how rude our people are?"

"Yes, though to tell the truth, at nine-forty-five I joined in the clapping myself. After all, it's most tiresome to sit waiting for an hour and fifteen minutes in the darkness."

"You said that she did come on in the end, didn't she?"

"Oh, most definitely. Somebody raised the curtain by mistake and we spotted the diva moving the piano toward the middle of the stage."

"Maria Callas?"

"Yes. She is thin, but quite powerful. She moved that heavy instrument all by herself. She was wearing a gorgeous evening gown. It was an unforgettable sight: the exquisitely delicate figure projected against the unwieldy black mass of the piano; it was really dramatic. I was so deeply moved I almost cried. It's a pity they lowered the curtain so quickly."

"I don't understand. Why did Miss Callas have to move the piano? Weren't there any stage hands around?"

"Of course there were."

"Where?"

"At the box office. After the concert I remembered that it was not the clerk who had sold me my ticket but two burly fellows in overalls. It seems that Presence Sulzbaum had not paid them in advance, so they impounded the box-office receipts that night."

"Did the impresario not protest?"

"He couldn't. He was tied to a chair and gagged

with a handkerchief."

"For goodness' sake! Didn't anyone intervene?"

"Of course they intervened. The musicians were looking all over the building for Presence. You see, Sulzbaum's checks had bounced and the orchestra committee headed by the drummer decided to apply moral pressure so he should pay the advance in cash before the opening of the concert, provided it opened at all, that is."

"But you said they had impounded the box-office receipts that night."

"That only covered the stage hands and porters."

"Was the house sold out?"

"What a question! After all, there is only one Callas in this world! On the other hand, Sulzbaum is a very experienced diver but as an impresario he's a greenhorn. Since this was his first show he went all out and hired one hundred and five musicians, thus even a sold-out hall would cover only half the cost of the orchestra and nothing else. I must admit that Sulzbaum gave proof of great courage. When the drummer discovered him and removed the handkerchief from his mouth he started shouting at the top of his voice: 'Rowdies! Pirates!' But the audience in the hall thought this was part of some opera they were rehearsing. By then it was ten-thirty and we were rather upset, when Maria Callas suddenly showed up."

"In front of the curtain?"

"Yes, this time in front of the curtain. We started clapping like mad. However, what she did was a little unconventional. She had come in from the wings carrying a burning candle, and now, crouching low, she moved along the footlights. She seemed to be looking for the microphone cables. As I told you, the sound engineer and the electricians were striking because of the advance and she was trying to hook up the sound system all by herself."

"How silly!"

"Of course. After all, she's only a singer and not an electrician. Using a pair of pliers, she tried to remove the nails holding the microphone cable to the planks. In the end the sound engineer took pity on her, came onstage and removed her bodily. Then the musicians started filing into the pit."

"So they got their money after all?"

"No, promissory notes. Naturally, they did not begin playing right away, but first sent the drummer to a bank manager who lived nearby and had him check whether the notes could be cashed right away. That wasted another forty minutes."

"The audience took all this quietly?"

"There was sporadic rioting. Here and there people smashed their seats and tossed the backs onto the stage. Animals, I'm telling you. Personally, I felt like sinking into the floor, I was so ashamed of the way I was behaving. What would Maria Callas think of us, right? But she was a sport. At midnight she came out in front of the curtain and gave a few numbers."

"Arias?"

"No, acrobatic dances. Remember, the loudspeakers were not turned on until the return of the drummer from the bank manager's. The audience received her exercises with stormy applause, especially the perfect crab she did by candlelight."

"Miss Callas is a very versatile artist."

"Indeed she is. But she had to interrupt the show because all the lights went on in the hall. What happened was that Sulzbaum had chewed through his bonds and escaped from the box office. A dramatic chase then ensued. The musicians knew that Sulzbaum was hiding somewhere in the building because the winds were guarding all the exits. They searched among the audience as well, since they suspected that Sulzbaum could have mingled with it or else was hiding under a seat. Finally, a few minutes before one A.M., if I'm not mistaken, they located him in the conductor's room."

"What happened?"

"While the strings were searching the basement storeroom, the conductor discovered Sulzbaum perched atop one of the big spotlights and took him prisoner. He intended getting out of him in advance at least his fee for four days, so he dragged Sulzbaum into the drawing room and started torturing him. Sulzbaum withstood the physical pain manfully, but yelled like an animal when the conductor extinguished a cigarette on his buttocks. That in fact was how the committee discovered him."

"By the way, what did the bank manager say?"

"He told the drummer that the notes were no good. So the disappointed committee members came and closed in on Presence. They prepared to lynch the impresario, but the drummer, conscious of his civic responsibility, pointed out to the committee that the time was two-fifteen A.M. and they should show some consideration for the public. 'These people have paid good money, boys. They are entitled to some artistic enjoyment.' This is what the drummer said, and under his soothing influence they agreed that the orchestra should go into the pit and play the overture as a gesture of good will. If in the meantime Sulzbaum succeeded in mobilizing by telephone I£5,000 in cash, they even promised to play until the intermission."

"And Miss Callas?"

"She moved along the aisles and entertained the audience with card tricks. She's very agile, Miss Callas is. Someone asked her how she liked our country, but we couldn't make out her reply because just then the loudspeakers went on and broadcast the noisy quarrel between Sulzbaum and the committee. Particularly discordant were the screeches of a stage hand who kept repeating, 'A hundred fifty in my hand or else I drop the scenery on her!' "

"Why didn't the police intervene?"

"What has the police got to do with an organized labor wage dispute? And besides, the single officer on duty there went home at three-thirty A.M. By the way, it was the mistake of his life, because at four A.M. Miss Callas broke down and deposited a certain sum with the committee as a guarantee for regular payments during the coming weeks' victory parade. Thereupon the orchestra again assembled, the curtain went up and she came onstage."

"How did Miss Callas sing?"

"Very beautifully. Though it is said that she was not her usual self this time. You know, these singers, they have their ups and downs."

❦ Ever since his brothers sold young Joseph at a bargain price to Potiphar, claiming he was a graduate interpreter of dreams, the prestige of foreign experts in this part of the world has been on a constant ascent. Even in our country they are a privileged class. Yugoslav football coaches, French nuclear physicists and Alaskan mink growers enjoy scandalously high salaries, battleship-sized motorcars and secretaries with loose morals, and all this to make them stay and admit the fact that, after all, we know a little better.

How to Deal with Know-It-All Experts

As soon as the process for the production of synthetic gasoline from grapefruit received its Israeli patent, the green light was given for the construction of the plant. The revolutionary invention came as an eleventh-hour windfall to save the country from its recurrent budgetary crises. It was expected to fuel the country's ever-growing fleet of cars almost at no cost.

The necessary foreign currency was promptly mobilized in Argentina, while the government chipped in with local capital.

Six months later an imposing industrial compound had risen not far from a well-known textile factory in the south. The machinery was ordered in Switzerland according to the specifications prepared by a visiting Italian engineer. And hardly a year later the green light was given for Grapoline Enterprises to start operations.

The glittering opening ceremony was attended by the beaming foreign investors, government officials and assorted plant managers and administrators. In his brief address, the Minister explained that at long last we were going to have a factory which would never suffer from lack of raw materials.

The Argentinian Ambassador then pressed a mink-coated button, and the giant machines started turning in an earsplitting yet gay clatter and rumble. Mountains of grapefruit moved on conveyor belts to the grinders and from there to the presses and the cracking unit. And barely a few minutes later there emerged from the end pipe the first drops of the precious golden liquid for the sake of which so much human blood had been spilled in the past.

And then it happened.

The ceremony was at its height when the Argentinian Ambassador's little son hopped over to the huge gasoline tank, dipped in a finger, licked it, and, before he could be stopped, repeated the process several times. The horrified spectators summoned a doctor, who, however, could find no adverse effects.

The liquid which came out of the pipes had an excellent taste. Far from being gasoline, it was ready-to-drink grapefruit juice.

For a whole week the country was in the grip of the resounding scandal. The authorities started an investigation, seeking those responsible for the affair, while the latter placed the blame squarely on the irresponsible authorities. Accusations and counter-accusations were bandied freely. For some reason or other, the Italian engineer had left for Tangier an hour before the Grapoline ceremony was due to start. He was never heard of again. The sensation-hungry press came out with inflammatory editorials which could well have shaken the public's confidence in the authorities. The papers in question were duly sued.

According to the charge sheet, the editorials had claimed, among other things, that the plant's product, namely grapefruit juice, was of a very poor quality, and that, in the view of the plaintiffs, was malicious libel. The damages claimed amounted to I£200,000. Fortunately the foreign investors had not noticed anything and left the country in high spirits.

Not so the government.

The investigating committee met in emergency session and after extensive deliberations came to the conclusion that the only thing the government could do was to invite at once an international authority on the subject to stay here for a year or two and find out why no gasoline came out of the pipes, and also to advise on what was to be done.

Joe Blow, the international authority on oil and gunboats, arrived and asked to see the Grapoline works without delay. For three full days he snooped around the factory, checked its equipment and then informed the general manager at whose initiative, by the way, the plant had been set up, "Sorry, but you can't make gasoline out of grapefruit."

"All right," the manager said, "but all the same—"

"What all the same? I said it's impossible. What I recommend is that you discard most of the machinery and maybe you'll be able to produce all sorts of fruit juices."

Thereupon the manager grabbed the expert by the scruff of his neck and lifted him off the floor.

"Listen, sir," he hissed. "We don't need your silly advice, all right? We have invested astronomical sums of money in this plant and energy and enthusiasm and lots of propaganda, and all that not simply so as to build another juice bottling plant! We must produce gasoline here and, what's more, out of grapefruit!"

"Sorry, it can't be done. And now please put me down."

The Deputy Minister offered Joe Blow a cigar.

"I greatly enjoyed your report, sir," he said, "though I must say it disappointed me in no small measure. I am referring particularly to the following remark which in my opinion is somewhat exaggerated: 'Setting up a plant of this nature reveals a shocking lack of responsibility even of the most infantile nature, etc.' Now would you call this a constructive approach? It is as if you were proclaiming that all of us here are a bunch of incompetents! You, sir, did not waste on us even one word of praise for our superhuman efforts in setting up the plant, nor did you find a single excuse justifying its existence to the taxpayers. We did not expect such hostile behavior from a world-famous expert, who, by the way, costs us a lot of foreign currency."

The Deputy Minister broke into sobs and this made a deep impression on the expert.

"But what can I do, your Excellency?" Joe Blow mumbled. "You just can't make gasoline out of grapefruit."

"Then at least write in your report that we are on the threshold of a scientific breakthrough. That would be a great help politically."

"I'm really sorry, but there's not a chance."

"All right," the Deputy Minister spluttered, "if that's the way you want it!"

Next day they moved Joe Blow from his luxury hotel to a crummy place in Jaffa and also wired his room for Oriental music. The payment of his salary became bogged down in red tape and the car which until then had been at his disposal was taken away from him.

The expert walked around, exhausted and sweating, but his spirit was unbroken.

"No," he croaked, "there's no gasoline in grapefruit! No and no!"

Next they sent him on an intensive trade-union course on the development of the country. The authorities had high expectations for the six-month course, but the expert was made of sterner stuff.

"Impossible," he breathed, unbroken, at the end of the ordeal. "Out of the question!"

From then on he was kept incommunicado and the Grapoline director spoke to him quite unequivocally.

"Either you write a proper report, my boy, or you'll come to a very sad end indeed!" he shouted. "What do you want? What have we done to you? Why did you come here? Or maybe you want to blackmail us? All right! We are in a tight spot. Let's talk terms."

Here the director pulled out of his pocket a completed report, reading as follows: "The Grapoline plant and everything round it is quite all right. No doubt about it: This is the work of a genius. Everything is going to turn out all right. May the Almighty bless the initiative of this marvelous enterprise.

Sincerely yours,

———

International Authority"

"On the dotted line!"

"No!" the expert obstinately refused. "I'd rather die!"

That night they caught Joe Blow at Lydda Airport trying to stow away in the toilet of an outgoing plane.

The police immediately arrested the unrepentant expert and jailed him until the end of the investigation into the circumstances of this clear case of economic sabotage.

Two weeks later the expert was visited in his cell by the director, accompanied by two wide-shouldered local experts.

"Well, can one get gasoline out of grapefruit?"

The expert cowered in a corner and breathed with difficulty.

"No," he groaned. "If you must know, it's actually more likely the other way round: grapefruit out of gasoline."

"All right," the director said, "you'll never get out of here alive!"

About a month later Joe Blow succeeded in sawing through the bars of his cell with his comb and broke out of the prison. A police dragnet was thrown out but did not catch him. There were rumors that the expert had crossed the border disguised as an infiltrator, but some people say that to this day he is employed as an unskilled laborer in the Negev.

The official communiqué tersely announced that "the international expert on oil and gunboats has left the country for technical reasons several years before the expiration of his contract. His report is still under study, but apparently contains nothing worthy of note."

By the way, the Grapoline plant is now manufacturing synthetic grapefruit juice. They say it's excellent. An international expert has been invited to taste it.

🕊 *As this book goes to press, the Israeli government owes various foreign creditors about four billion dollars and still goes on taking loans at usurious rates of interest wherever it can get them. Clearly the government bets on a global nuclear war which would automatically absolve all debts, but we, simple citizens, worry all the same that one of these days they'll try to collect from us. Therefore we try to register our debts in the wife's name.*

Family Affair

The other night I dreamt I was married to the government. That is she, the government, was my wife, quite a decent woman, really, though a little on the stout side and leaning toward baldness. I watched her out of the corner of my eye while she cooked dinner for twenty-six persons.

"But, darling," I admonished her, "apart from us there are just the three kids."

"And what if some guests drop in unexpectedly?"

She has an answer for everything. A few days ago I kicked up a row when I found that we owed the delicatessen eight billion pounds, whereupon she turned on me and screamed that she doesn't spend a single superfluous penny, that people are always wondering how she manages on what I give her, that she hasn't got a rag to wear and that her friends always say to her, "Government, your husband simply does not appreciate what a pearl of a wife he has," and so on, and so on.

The night I had that dream I was a little upset.

"Look, my dear," I reminded Government in the kitchen, "only the other day I gave you two billions; where the hell are they?"

"Gone," she answered. "Believe me, I didn't steal them. They are simply gone! Celery is more expensive since last week. I paid the laundry, and whitewashing the kitchen cost I£30 alone."

"All right," I said, "but that's still not two billions."

"So I don't know!" Government flared up. "I can't give you an exact account for every pound I spend. I'm an honest woman. I care only for my family."

"I want to know where my money is going."

I was rather nervous. My wife took off her apron and drew up to her considerable full height.

"Tell me," she sneered, "where else would you like me to skimp?"

"Maybe," I said, "you don't need three cars."

"Do you want me to walk?"

"And the pastry shop? Why do you have to have breakfast in the most expensive pastry shop in town?"

"I'm simply maintaining your status."

"But we are beggars," I roared. "All I earn is I£460 a month!"

"Ephraim, you are hysterical," said Government. "Please, take the garbage downstairs."

About twelve tons had accumulated in our garbage cans, three tons of metal shavings, a ton of phosphates and lots of textiles and silica sand. I dragged it up the mountain of refuse in front of our house, fuming as I trudged up its slope. It is terribly upsetting that a man has to work like an animal, doing overtime, breaking his back, and in the end cannot even get an explanation from his wife what she's spending his money on. Last week, when they charged us I£80 million interest at the bank I blew my top.

"How do you do it?" I roared. "How?"

She answered coldly, "I took out insurance for the children. Do you want to leave the children without insurance?"

I came in from the dunghill in a filthy mood.

"Listen," I said to the wife, "either you lower expenses or I leave you!"

"Why?"

"I'll tell you why! Because you can't spend more than I have, that's why! I've never seen a housewife who decides beforehand how much she'll feel like spending on groceries during the coming year and then expects her husband to earn accordingly. It ought to be exactly the other way around."

"But—"

"Now I'm talking, Government!" I yelled. "I bring home I£460 a month. With that you'll have to make do and that's that!"

"How?"

"That's none of my bloody business! Cut down expenses! Fire your five servants, sell the silver candlesticks, don't cook on Saturdays—I don't care how!"

"All right, all right," the wife soothed me. "Don't get so excited. Give us a kiss."

I brushed my lips against her bald pate and ever since, we, the government and I, live in happiness and connubial harmony, until the end of the present financial year.

❦ *It is a regrettable fact, but a fact all the same, that orderliness and accuracy are in direct proportion to geographic location. As you move northward in the direction of the happy countries blessed with cool climates, trains, planes and watches are progressively more punctual, the mail and your breathing are more regular and workers as a rule work.*

Israel, it will be remembered, is a subtropical country.

The Elusive Ginger

Last week a minor hitch occurred in the prototype of the excellent locally produced aircraft, the Arava. A few days before its departure for the Paris Air Show where it was expected to set off a stampede of buyers, it landed sans right wheel and was left lying on its belly like a wounded sparrow. But the matter is being dealt with, the management reported. Arava will still make it to the show only slightly late; anyway, the opening is just one big bore. It is said that the hitch was not due to anything really serious but simply to a series of coincidences. There is no reason to get upset, really; everything is under control; don't worry.

The investigation continues. Though he knows very little about aeronautics and has not received any data on the mishap, this writer feels eminently qualified to submit his vital testimony on the reasons for the southpaw landing. Simply from experience and from time-proven Mediterranean calculations, we claim that the cause of the mishap was that the keys were with Ginger.

There couldn't possibly be any other reason.

To be more exact, let us reconstruct all the details. After the last test flight, the pilot told Shlomo that he didn't like the sound of the wheels. But Shlomo had to settle something at City Hall, so he asked the gatekeeper to ring up Zimmerman in the workshop and ask him to have a look below or something. But Zimmerman was not in the building because Mondays he always leaves at 2:30 and the gatekeeper, too, was temporary because the old chap had gone for urological tests in the morning. And he didn't know where Zimmerman lives—who was this Zimmerman anyway?—and the switchboard didn't answer either because Ziva had gone to Haifa to get something out of customs. The only plant list with the addresses of Zimmerman and the mechanics was locked up in a drawer, but Ginger had taken the key and had gone downstairs. They looked for him in the cafeteria, but he had left ten minutes before and he has no telephone at home and he has the key and you can't do a thing. And thus the Arava took off on a prayer and landed on a wheel, but it's all right. Most of the parts were recovered from the runway.

So there is absolutely no need for further investigation; things just had to happen this way. They always happen like that. Almost every ambitious national campaign in our Mediterranean homeland eventually runs aground because Ginger has got the key. Whenever we happen into the vicinity of any huge enterprise, an old established factory, a brand-new shopping center, the Ministry for Foreign Affairs, a film studio, a bus terminal, and everything is topsy-turvy and the staff runs berserk and ask Ziva for a line, and pounds the door of the locked storeroom, on every such hectic occasion there appears at the end of the passage a very fat man with an apoplectic face who shouts, "Where is the key?"

"Ginger has got it," Avigdor answers, hugging the wall.

"Where is Ginger?"

The loudspeakers blare all over the plant, "Ginger, Kooti is looking for you. Go to his office at once with the keys! Ginger, can you hear me?"

Ginger isn't there. That, in fact, is one of Ginger's remarkable qualities—that he isn't there. He is gone. With the keys. Only fifteen minutes ago he was seen near the toilets, but he must have gone out or something. He lives in the provinces and has no telephone at home. Zimmerman has his new address, but he is not in the building.

To further the current investigation, we herewith take pleasure in giving an exact description of Ginger. Well, first and foremost he is ginger-haired, squat, wears an open-necked shirt and corduroy trousers, a congenitally squashed nose, a hairy chest, water-blue eyes; he is strong as a horse, has sired two sons and a daughter and sports a gap between his teeth, the exact location of which varies from specimen to specimen. Rarely, maybe once a year, mostly in September, one can catch a glimpse of Ginger in the flesh walking up the stairs with dangling keys. At such times Kooti only narrowly avoids a fit.

"Listen, Ginger," the fat man roars, purple in the face. "Where in the hell have you been?"

"In the stores," Ginger says. "Where else could I have been?"

"They said you had gone out."

"Nonsense."

Then and there Ginger is ordered to have copies cut of all his keys and hand them over to Shlomo. But

Ginger doesn't order them on principle, and besides
Shlomo is at loggerheads with Kooti because of the de-
ductions from the resthouse grant which the committee
did not approve before the holidays. There is one theory
according to which there is a single Ginger in the whole
country who tours the big manufacturing concerns with
a key, and that's why he cannot be found anywhere.
Anyway, he belongs in our fascinating scenery like the
flies and the postal strike. One can hardly visualize our
lives without him. It is said that in one of the largest
arms factories they handcuffed him to a lathe, and for
two full hours he was visible to the naked eye. But then
he slipped his hands out and left and ever since no arms
are being manufactured and the earth is without form
and void, and the spirit of Ginger moves over the deep
and only Zimmerman knows his new address and he is
not in the building. Let's sing the praises of Ginger,
who has the key.

❧ Since we are nearing the end of this book, here is something about the end, with fervent hopes for human wisdom which is steadily growing, more's the pity. Quite a funny story. For the time being at least.

Atoms for the Masses

Shultheiss stopped me at the corner of Arlosoroff Street.

"Give me a ride to the parcel post, will you?" he said. "I've got to go there urgently."

I let him in. Shultheiss was very nervous. I asked him what was the matter.

"Don't ask me. My brother-in-law has sent me an atom bomb from Germany."

"What?"

"Yes, shocking, isn't it? Though I read in a magazine that a German invention had now turned the manufacture of nuclear devices into a simple and inexpensive process, applicable everywhere. But to send it in a parcel?"

"Very odd, I must say."

"As of now it looks as if the man in the street will be able to afford it. Here is my brother-in-law's letter: 'P.S.' Friedrich writes, 'I've got a little surprise for you. Today I airmailed you an atom bomb. Have a nice time!' "

"He's overdoing it."

"Friedrich always was generous," Shultheiss said. "Now what am I going to do with a bomb?"

"I don't know. I never had one."

"Beatrice is driving me nuts. 'I don't want nuclear weapons in my house!' she yelled at me as I left. 'I've got enough troubles with the kid!' So help me, she's right. I myself would hate to have Danny playing with an atom bomb. I wouldn't stand for it. He dismantles everything he comes across. Just imagine! And besides, where am I going to keep the bomb? In the refrigerator?"

"Is it a big one, the bomb?"

"I haven't the faintest. I'm not an expert. I'll read the instructions. Maybe I'll understand them. Anyway, I hope he didn't buy the largest size. We've got a very small freezer. But Beatrice will throw it out anyway. Believe me, if Friedrich were not so sensitive I would send it right back. Who needs an atom bomb? Do you think they'll let me test it? Not here—in the Negev Desert."

"I suppose if you've got the right connections—"

"I'm sure I'll have lots of trouble because of this. Our neighbors, you know what they're like. They are already calling us snobs. So I can't blame my wife if she wants to get rid of the bomb. 'Danny coughs anyway all day long,' she said to me. 'Sell it!' Would you be interested?"

"Not really."

"I see. Beatrice thinks the government will be only too glad to buy it. I said to her, Big deal! And if my brother-in-law ever visits us and asks, 'Well, and where is the bomb I sent you?' What am I going to tell him? 'I sold it, Friedrich'?"

"Then don't sell it."

"It's not as simple as that. A certain responsibility goes with it. It's also a big bother. First of all, to participate in all those disarmament conferences. It's absurd!

Who has time for such nonsense?"

"China, England," I enumerated them, "France, the Soviet Union, the United States of America, Shultheiss."

"No, I won't go."

"Why not?"

"I'm too shy and I can't make speeches. Besides, I've got just one bomb, so what will they ask me to do? That I should destroy my bomb. I know their kind. But I am not going to destroy anything. How will I know that the Chinese, too, have destroyed their stockpile, right?"

"Right."

"I'm telling you, this German invention is going to set the whole world topsy-turvy. A private person cannot afford such expenses."

"What expenses?"

"Insurance! Excuse me, but I couldn't possibly take the risk of the bomb's exploding in the house. Then the bomb could break down. Who's going to repair it? Maybe Stuks, the plumber?"

"Why should it break down? It's a brand-new bomb."

"I assume a one-year guarantee goes with it. But as a rule these guarantees don't apply to natural disasters or wars. It's ridiculous, after all. When do you use an atom bomb? In war!"

"Do you actually want to use it?"

"You bet!"

"How are you going to send it?"

"By mail."

Shultheiss took a firm grip on himself.

"As a matter of fact," he said, "I don't care. So I'll have a bomb at home. The Big Powers don't ever use theirs either. I'll keep it, just in case. If you must know, whenever I think of it, that I'll have an atom bomb at home, I feel good!"

"Why?"

"I don't know. I feel good. It gives you a lot of self-assurance. Providing Danny doesn't discover it . . ."

We reached the parcel post. Shultheiss paid I£46 duty and I£26 luxury tax.

"Careful," he warned the porters. "There's a bomb inside."

It was a smallish parcel. Two cops helped us to open it. With bated breath we took out a garishly colored box bearing the inscription: "Long live the atom! A perfect replica of the atom bomb, flashes and whistles. Fun for children and adults!"

"Friedrich is crazy," Shultheiss fumed. "This is for Danny's birthday." Then he added with a dreamy look in his eyes, "I had got used to the idea."

❧ *Last but not least, let us pour out our unbridled and always topical ire on the most destructive force in human experience, the sweetest snake you can buy for a monthly salary.*

The Typist

This writer has been writing a weekly column for twenty years now. It seems only appropriate, therefore, on this solemn occasion to devote these lines, for once, to the reader for whom they are written week after week. Or rather to the first reader of the column who is nobody else but the office typist to whom we dedicate it while it is still fresh and tender—because we have no other choice.

For twenty years we kept quiet. Now the time has come to speak up.

Not as if we have anything against typists as a profession protected by the trade-union. Quite the contrary. We appreciate the technical assistance they extend to us writers. The only complaint we have against them is that they are eroding us from within.

What are we driving at?

What we are driving at is that you compose at home an extremely funny story on the devaluation of the Israeli pound, and you toil on this little opus of yours for three days and two nights, polish it, add to it, cut it and restore some of the cuts, until you attain relative perfection. Then you go to the office, sit down next to Lilly, the chief typist, and dictate to her, hardly able to suppress your happy giggles.

"Devaluation . . ."

"What?" Lilly says. "Again?"

And with that she has finished us off. We are already lying on the floor like a bird pierced by an arrow and shall never again be able to get up. With one word Wonder Lilly has succeeded in bringing down on our head the whole edifice on which we had worked so hard for three days and two nights. We realize in a flash that our subject matter is stale, much too much has already been written on devaluation, nobody gives a damn any longer, it's a deadly bore.

"Again?"

Wonder Lilly doesn't say "again" because she wants to kill us; she is simply unable to realize that she is our first reader. She does not feel the heavy responsibility that rests on the public at a premiere; she simply wants to go home at 1:45 P.M. Naturally we go on dictating in a gay voice as befits a professional clown, but our heart is bleeding. We no longer believe in the story on devaluation. We were defeated before the first shot was fired. "Again?" Our last hope is that when we come to the point of the story, then Lilly will smile—we don't dare hope that she will actually laugh—and thereby restore some of our self-respect, because that part . . . with the new taxes . . . is so funny . . .

We look at Lilly from the side, from a difficult angle, with bated breath. Maybe . . .

Lilly doesn't laugh. She sits poker-faced at the typewriter and looks into the air dreamily. Her fingers drum a tattoo on the keys, as if she were saying: At 1:45 we are going, sir.

We look at the paper in the typewriter.

"The Minister of Finance called four new taxis . . ."

"Lilly," we whisper brokenhearted, "what taxis?"

"Oh, it's taxes," Lilly says. "Why didn't you say so?"

Lilly types whatever she hears. She would type the greatest nonsense without batting an eyelid. Before our mind's eye there appears the main headline of the special edition: "Killed His Typist While Dictating to Her—'She Didn't Listen,' the Writer Said, Crying Hysterically—the Third Typist to Fall Victim to His Anger in the Last Two Years."

Yes, we forgot to point out that there are three typists in the office.

Wonder Lilly is the hardest of the lot. Bathsheba is an angel and Estherke is so-so.

To dictate to Bathsheba is a dream. She participates in the writing of the story from the beginning to the end. You just mention the headline "Devaluation" and she is seized by an attack of laughter.

"Devaluation!" she almost chokes with laughter. "Devaluation? Devaluation! Where do you get those ideas?"

I love Bathsheba. There is something in that girl. After each story she gets up, her face shining, and exclaims, "Excellent!"

She has a fantastic sense of timing. All you have to do is raise your voice a little, produce an impish smile or just give her a slight nudge with your elbow and Bathsheba immediately gets the hint and breaks into uninhibited, elementary laughter. An experienced writer could get out of Bathsheba a dozen wild guffaws per story, at least five pleasurable sighs and a surefire fainting at the end. Writing with Bathsheba is not work but an organized victory parade. Bathsheba has shining black eyes and a warm womanly heart.

Only she has no time. Because Bathsheba is grabbed by the editors as if she were a hotcake. First thing in the morning people are registering with her. Everybody wants to be sure of getting her, six writers looking for a typist.

"You know what?" the hypocrites tell us. "Why don't you dictate to Estherke?"

Estherke is not bad. Her reactions are satisfactory, and on good days she even laughs. Yes, sometimes the tears flow from her eyes in the middle of a good story of mine. We are sitting next to her enjoying the gay laughter which breaks out of Estherke's throat and nod our head with unconcealed pleasure.

"Come, come, enough really. What's so funny here?"

"Your accent." Estherke rolls on the floor. "Your accent."

That is, she is not too bright; she carries us to our grave every time we dictate to her. A few days ago, for instance, we dictated to her a hard-hitting story about that chairman of the Students' Association who had publicly offended the Prime Minister.

"To call the Prime Minister a liar is without doubt an act of heroism," we dictated to Estherke with sarcasm. "Good show, young man!"

Here Estherke stopped typing and looked at us with eyes wide open.

"Good for you," she whispered enthusiastically. "That student really is some guy! And how the others attacked him!"

We blanched.

"Listen, my girl," we mumbled, "this is written tongue-in-cheek, ironically. Don't you see?"

"Of course," Estherke answers with downcast eyes.

"If you say so."

Still she's gold compared with Wonder Lilly, to whom we are dictating this story right now. The time is 1:40. She is already arranging her purse, ready for the starter's gun, and rings someone to tell him to wait for her at 2:46. I wonder if she realizes that this story is about her. She has a bemused expression on her face, but nothing seems to trouble her. Her eyes are fixed on the ceiling. As a matter of fact I've finished the story. I stopped dictating, but Lilly remains seated and waits for the continuation, her eyes now roaming the shelves of the supermarket across the street.

Silence.

"What?" she asks. "Is this the end?"

"Yes."

She gets up without another word. I am shrinking on my chair. This is our twentieth anniversary.

We turn on her in a trembling voice. "Well, how is it?"

"What?" Lilly asks, combing her hair. "How is what?"

"The story."

"Weak," answers Lilly. "I think I'll have to change the ribbon."

A broken old man about an inch tall gets up from our chair and crawls on all fours toward the door. The typists are killing us, slowly but relentlessly. One of these nights while dictating we'll break up into grains of sand. That's all.

DATE DUE
